The Br...
Medical Asso...

FAMILY DOCTOR GUIDE

STRESS

The British Medical Association

FAMILY DOCTOR GUIDE *to*

STRESS

PROFESSOR GREG WILKINSON

MEDICAL EDITOR
DR. TONY SMITH

DORLING KINDERSLEY
LONDON • NEW YORK • SYDNEY • MOSCOW
www.dk.com

IMPORTANT

This book is not designed as a substitute for personal medical advice but as a supplement to that advice for the patient who wishes to understand more about his/her condition.

Before taking any form of treatment **YOU SHOULD ALWAYS CONSULT YOUR MEDICAL PRACTITIONER.**

In particular (without limit) you should note that advances in medical science occur rapidly and some of the information contained in this book about drugs and treatment may very soon be out of date.

PLEASE NOTE

The author regrets that he cannot enter into any correspondence with readers.

A DORLING KINDERSLEY BOOK
www.dk.com

Senior Editor Mary Lindsay
Senior Designer Sarah Hall
Project Editor David Tombesi-Walton
Designer Laura Watson
DTP Designer Jason Little
Production Controller Michelle Thomas

Managing Editor Stephanie Jackson
Managing Art Editor Nigel Duffield

Produced for Dorling Kindersley Limited by
Design Revolution, Queens Park Villa,
30 West Drive, Brighton, East Sussex BN2 2GE.
Editorial Manager Ian Whitelaw
Art Director Fiona Roberts
Editor Julie Whitaker
Designer Vanessa Good

Published in Great Britain in 1999 by
Dorling Kindersley Limited,
9 Henrietta Street, London WC2E 8PS

2 4 6 8 10 9 7 5 3 1

A CIP catalogue record for this book is available from the British Library

ISBN 0 7513 0681 9

Reproduced by Colourscan, Singapore
Printed in Hong Kong by Wing King Tong

Contents

Coping with stress

What causes stress? Anything that makes you tense, angry, frustrated or unhappy. It may be thinking about next week's driving test or a visit from a difficult relative, the choices you have to make when moving house or getting married, an accident or injury, the seemingly unrelenting pressures of work or the unavoidable burden of coping with a death in the family.

A survey by the Health and Safety Executive has shown that half a million Britons suffer illnesses related to stress at work – and this is probably an underestimate! Factors that stress some people give others excitement. Racing drivers and mountaineers seem to thrive on physical challenges. Some people enjoy the excitement of going to sea in bad weather, and they join the lifeboat crew. Others choose to work on high buildings and rooftops. So one person's stress may be another person's pleasure.

In fact, a certain amount of stress is good for us. When we have to face up to a challenge or we are made to get on with some job we don't want to do, we often find that we can achieve the targets we have been set. We then feel

JUGGLING TASKS
Trying to balance a family and a career is a common cause of stress in the lives of many working people.

Falling Out
Stress becomes a major concern when it begins to affect our relationships, either at home or at work.

a lot better having done it. Facing challenges and overcoming them stops us from getting bored. In fact, many people deliberately create mild stress in their lives to overcome periods of dull routine. Too much stress, however, affects our health and well-being, and may interfere with our jobs and our social lives. Repeated, continuing, severe stress has a weakening and demoralising effect, which may make it more difficult to do anything about the factors that are causing the stress. Just how we respond to pressure is determined by our characters, and by our personal disabilities or illnesses. These dictate how we react to difficulties with relationships, both at home and in the working environment, and also to practical problems that arise over money, work and housing.

Adjusting to Stress

As we grow and mature we become better at knowing what to expect in our everyday life, and what to do about the things that upset us. We become better at dealing with the unexpected. We learn to make adjustments in attitude and in the way we behave, in order to understand and to cope. Usually this is fairly straightforward and we are hardly aware that we are 'coping with stress'.

When events of major importance take place, however, such as marriage, birth or the death of someone close, our reactions and the way we cope are more obvious to us.

In order to live successfully with stress, we need to spend some time considering the sources of stress in our lives and whether our physical and emotional responses to these are sensible and useful, or are preventing us from coping and taking control. Although studies show that the ability to cope is partly inborn, it is also a question of training, upbringing and practice.

OVERCOMING STRESS

There is every reason to be optimistic that you will be able to overcome stress that is taking over your life. There are several simple and effective methods that can be used to reduce and overcome stress, and, in most cases, these self-help solutions are very successful.

Although almost everyone is under some form of stress, only a few ever respond by developing a physical or emotional illness that requires specialist help.

KEY POINTS

- Stress is caused by anything that makes you tense, angry, frustrated or unhappy.
- One person's stress may be someone else's enjoyment.
- A certain level of stress is good for us.
- Too much stress affects our health and well-being.
- There is every reason to be optimistic that you will be able to overcome stress in your life.

Finding a balance

Stressed or Challenged?
Different people react to events in different ways. A situation that one person regards as an exciting and challenging opportunity – like a tight deadline at work – may be seen by another as unbearably stressful.

I have already said that stress can be both a good thing – a motivator – and a bad thing. Furthermore, what is stressful may not only vary from one person to another, but can change for one individual from year to year.

This is because the way that stress affects us depends on a balance between the demand made by the event(s) causing the stress and our ability to cope (which can vary considerably). Too large an imbalance between demand and ability to cope may result in the sort of stress that is not good for us. Looked at in a slightly different way, the overall level of stress depends on a complicated balance that takes account of the stressful event, our response to this in terms of physical effects, emotions and outward behaviour, and how significant the event is to us (is it something that makes us very happy, deeply sad or is it not too important?).

For example, if John Smith, who has a large mortgage, a wife, three children and a job that he enjoys and which is important to him, is made redundant, he is put under a great deal of stress. The event is of major significance to him, and he may suffer physical symptoms (inability to sleep, eat or relax) and emotional reactions (bursts of anger and irritation) that affect his outward behaviour.

Jill Brown, on the other hand, is 23 years old, highly qualified, with no responsibilities and a job that she finds boring. If she is made redundant, she may not be shattered. Instead, she may feel that the event has forced her to make a long overdue change, and she may be relieved and relaxed, feeling better than she has done in ages. In this case, stress has a positive side and is needed to introduce a necessary element of change in her life. We can see from this that similar stress events may bring out entirely different responses in different people.

How Stress Adds Up

Degree of stress	=	Potentially stressful events	+	Response to the events (physical, emotional or behavioural)	+	Significance of the events to us (happy, sad or indifferent)

KEY POINTS

- The way stress affects us depends on a balance between the demands made and our ability to cope.
- Physical symptoms of stress may sometimes result from an individual's inability to deal with it.

Sources of stress

We would all become extremely bored if nothing different or challenging ever happened in our lives. However, any major change needs to be balanced with our ability to cope with that particular change at the time in question.

Toddler Tantrums
Although children are an undeniable source of pleasure, the demands that they make can be one of the most potent sources of stress to a parent.

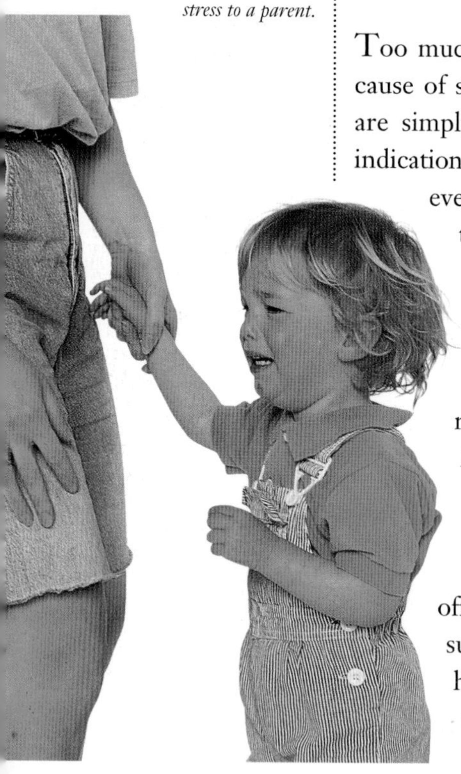

Too much change, too quickly, can often be a major cause of stress. The demands in these particular cases are simply far too great for our ability to cope. An indication of exactly how much stress various typical life events and social changes may cause is given in the table opposite.

In general, the greater the number of these events that happen to us in a given time, such as a year, and the higher their combined rating, the more likely we are to suffer a stress response, either emotional or physical. Moreover, the severity of the stress response is usually related to the significance of the events and changes experienced.

Remember that stress can also be triggered off by events that are usually regarded as pleasant, such as getting married, winning money or having a baby, as well as by unpleasant events such as losing a job, having an accident or the illness of someone in the family.

Life Events and Their Related Stress Levels

Many life events and social changes cause stress. Below is a list of common occurences, combined with a rating of the accompanying stress levels. The chart is adapted from Holmes and Rahe.

Life Event		Stress Level
Death of husband or wife	Personal injury or illness	Very high
Divorce or marital separation	Getting married	
Jail term	Loss of job	
Death of close family member	Moving house	
Marital reconciliation	Sex difficulties	High
Retirement	New child	
Serious illness of family member	Change of job	
Pregnancy	Money problems	
	Death of close friend	
Family arguments	Outstanding personal achievement	Moderate
Big mortgage or loan	Wife begins or stops work	
Legal action over debt	Start or finish of school	
Change in responsibilities at work	Change in living conditions	
Son or daughter leaving home	Revision of personal habits	
Trouble with in-laws	Trouble with boss	
Change in work hours or conditions	Change in sleeping habits	Low
Change in schools	Change in contact with family	
Change in recreation	Change in eating habits	
Change in church activities	Holidays	
Change in social activities	Christmas	
Small mortgage or loan	Minor violations of the law	

LIFE EVENTS

When evaluating the impact of life events and social changes as a cause of stress, we also need to take into account the fact that they tend to be particularly stressful when they are:

- Unpredictable
- Intense
- Major
- Unavoidable
- Unfamiliar
- Inevitable

Do be careful, however, not to take the contents of the table on p.13 too literally. It is common for people who feel stressed to search for the reason in past events, but some past events can be the result, rather than the cause, of the stress.

A feeling of not being able to cope with new duties or responsibilities, for example, may be the result of unrecognised stress rather than the stress being the result of a failure to cope with the situation.

So sources of stress lie mainly in these events in our lives and in our physical and emotional responses to such events. The cause may be obvious to us, in which case the way we need to react may be straightforward and clear cut, and depend on us making practical or emotional adjustments. In these circumstances, it may be easy to see where we should ask for help.

Often, though, the source of stress is not quite so obvious, and it may need some careful thought or talking through with others to bring it out in the open. Again, unrecognised illness may affect

What Factors Affect You?

To discover the sources of your stress, ask yourself whether there are any social, physical or emotional factors that are affecting you.

- How many teas/coffees/caffeinated drinks are you having?
- How much are you smoking?
- How much alcohol are you drinking?
- Are you taking enough exercise?
- Could you be ill?
- Is there some new element in your life?
- Has there been any change in your general circumstances?
- Have long-standing problems recently become worse?
- Is someone close to you facing difficulties that affect you?

our ability to cope, or there may be difficulties with relationships that we are not prepared to face. Sometimes, however, we may never find an answer, and very occasionally stress does come 'out of the blue'.

LIFE PHASES

You may get a clue about stress levels from considering the phase of life you are in. In the late teens, for example, many major decisions have to be made for the first time.

In mid-life, responsibilities are often at their heaviest and most dramatic. In old age, there may be illness, deaths in the family and money problems to cope with on your own.

You should also consider the phases of life that those close to you are in. Crying babies, bedtime blues, little monsters, know-it-alls, getting to school, teenage rebels – no parent gets it right every time. Even family mealtimes can be among the most stressful occasions in everyday life.

GROWING PAINS
Growing up can be a difficult time both for children and for parents. Arguments are common as children test the limits and try to establish their own sense of identity.

CONFLICTS IN YOUR LIFE

Ask yourself whether there is anything that you would like to sort out. For example:

- Do you have continual disagreements about someone or about something?
- Is some situation leaving you with a feeling that you are not good enough, or that it is all your fault?
- Are you taking, or being made to take, a new or unaccustomed role – or are you perhaps carrying, or being asked to carry, too much responsibility?
- Do you have unspoken fears or frustrations about your life?

Often stress is the result of a build-up of related and unrelated factors of these kinds. If you settle down quietly and list the stresses in your life, you may be surprised – and relieved – to discover some of the stresses are ones that you can eliminate.

THE WARNING SIGNS

The warning signs that stress may be affecting your health vary considerably from person to person. Most of us, however, tend to have our own usual stress response or 'fingerprint'.

This might be headaches in one person, or an outbreak of eczema or diarrhoea in another. Usually the first signs of stress are changes in our emotional life or behaviour, and at times the differences can become more noticeable to others than they are to us.

EMOTIONAL REACTIONS

The most important changes to watch out for are increases in tension, irritability and moodiness. Small irritations may seem unbearable if they come on top of stress, and can cause a major outburst or upset.

For example, the fact that the children want to play a board game when you have just come home from work and you simply want to sit down and relax may make you feel you want to put them up for adoption; or you may find that you have an overwhelming desire to perpetrate grievous bodily harm on your car when it refuses to start; and when the toaster will not pop up your slice of toast you have to be held back from attacking it with the bread knife.

There may also be changes in appetite or weight: some people lose interest in food, whereas others have a constant desire to eat. Your ability to cope at home and at work may become extremely variable: you may find you can't quite get round to paying the household bills, and are spurred into action only when the phone has been disconnected; and your brain seems to have moved into reverse gear at work so that the 'in tray' gets bigger and bigger. You smoke or drink (or both) more, which does, however, help fill in the time in the evening, as you seem to have difficulty in sleeping.

The box (right) gives some examples of different emotional reactions to stress. If you notice some of these signs or other people point them out to you, take notice; unless you take steps to protect yourself, you are at risk of experiencing increasing stress. You may not recognise all the signs at first, however, or you may have over-looked or ignored some for a variety of reasons.

You may also have to resist a tendency to regard the reactions as definite evidence of serious physical illness rather than a response to stress.

Emotional Reactions to Stress

- Feeling under pressure
- Feeling tense and unable to relax
- Feeling mentally drained
- Being constantly frightened or worried
- Increasing irritability and complaining
- Feelings of conflict
- Frustration and aggression
- Restlessness, increasing inability to concentrate or to complete tasks quickly
- Increased tearfulness
- Become more fussy, gloomy or suspicious
- Being unable to take decisions
- Impulses to run and hide
- Fears of imminent fainting, collapse or death
- Fears of social embarrassment or failure
- Lacking in ability to feel pleasure or enjoyment

PHYSICAL REACTIONS

Physical reactions to strong emotions were designed to save us in the days when we led the simple, dangerous life of the caveman. To Stone Age man these bodily responses meant fight or flight and prepared him for action; millions of years later they still do – which is very useful if a woolly mammoth is on the rampage, but not a great deal of help when we have just missed the last train or dropped the car keys down a drain in the road! What happens to our body is that our pulse and blood pressure increase, we breathe more rapidly and our ears, eyes and nose become more alert. These changes are the result of the action of stress hormones released into the blood circulation in response to the event.

When the stress response goes on for a long time, or occurs frequently and at the wrong time, it may lead to a wide range of unpleasant feelings. The number and the nature of physical feelings differ greatly between people, but the most common ones are listed in the box (left).

The most effective techniques for dealing with physical reactions to stress are controlled deep breathing and relaxation. These are discussed on pages 40–43. It is important to try to be relaxed throughout the day and not just during time you have set aside for leisure.

Physical Reactions to Stress

- Muscle tension
- Rapid, uneven or pounding heartbeat
- Fast, shallow breathing
- Sweating
- Dilated pupils
- Over-alertness
- Change in appetite
- Muscle weakness or trembling
- A sick feeling in the stomach
- Sleep problems
- Jumpiness
- Headaches
- Weakness of the limbs
- Indigestion
- Frequent urge to pass urine
- Chest discomfort
- Odd aches, pains or twitches
- Constipation or diarrhoea
- Tiredness and weakness
- Worsening of long-standing pain
- Constant restlessness and fidgeting
- Backache
- 'Pins and needles'
- Dry mouth or throat
- 'Butterflies' in the stomach

Physical and Mental Effects of Stress

Many parts of the body are affected by stress, leaving you susceptible to both physical and mental illnesses. Production of hormones such as adrenaline and cortisol increases, producing changes in heart rate, blood pressure and metabolism.

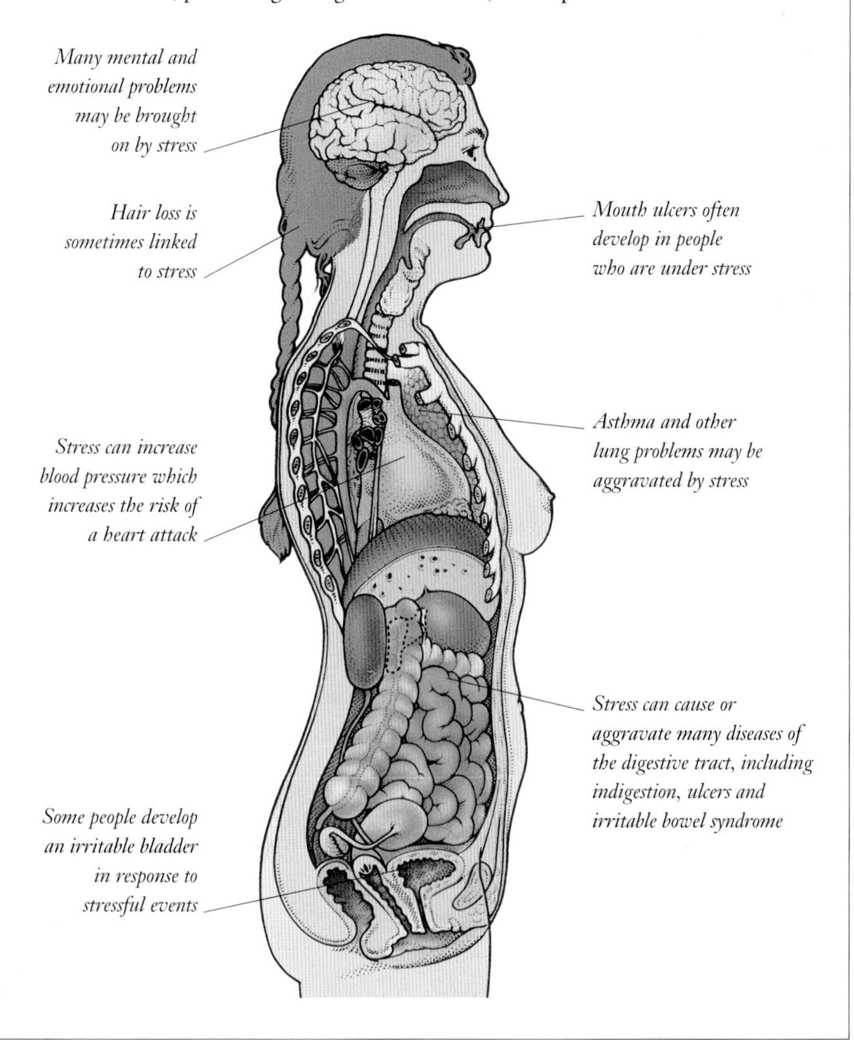

Try to start noticing bodily sensations, and whenever you feel physical reactions to stress try to relax your muscles. For example, drop your shoulders, then relax your facial and tummy muscles. If you can, stop what you are doing and rest: spend time quietly calming down and practise distracting yourself, deep breathing and relaxing your muscles. Start by taking a deep breath and slowing down your breathing. Take a deep breath, hold it in while you count up to three ('one hundred and one, one hundred and two, one hundred and three') and then slowly breathe out. Repeat this exercise and continue slow, relaxed breathing at around 10 breaths per minute. If you feel comfortable, you can increase to a 'six-second breath', counting one hundred and one to one hundred and six. (Fast, shallow breathing can increase physical reactions to stress.) Then slowly go back to what you were doing or carry on to where you were going – continuing to breathe slowly and deeply, distracting yourself and thinking constructively and positively about how you handled the situation and how you will deal with it should it recur.

BEHAVIOURAL REACTIONS

The behaviour of people under stress can change quite considerably. Often they hate to be alone and make efforts to seek support from family and friends. Some may become withdrawn and indifferent. They seem to have lost interest in others and even start to turn down invitations because of the effort involved.

They continually seek reassurance and can become indecisive – a trip to the supermarket for a packet of tea bags seems to require as much preparation as the ascent of Everest. They change their minds a lot and may speak fondly of someone one moment and find them completely useless the next. They may be tearful, difficult and complaining, and often expect others to be impossibly understanding of them. There may be a change in sexual habits (a loss of interest, an increase in casual sex or altered sexual preference), and the previously mild-mannered may become verbally or physically aggressive.

A person who used to be fairly relaxed may become rigid and obsessive, repeatedly checking locks and switches, for example, or regularly cleaning the oven at three in the morning when previously it was done once a year. Actions of this sort may be due to an effort to bring some order and certainty to the sense of confusion that they feel is surrounding them. Often a person under stress denies these behavioural changes, but they are usually very obvious to other people. Ask friends if they have noticed any changes in your behaviour, but don't be cross with them for telling the truth – remember that denying the obvious can be a sign of stress!

KEY POINTS

- Too much change too quickly can be a cause of stress.
- Stress can be caused by pleasant and unpleasant events.
- The cause of stress may not always be apparent.
- Usually stress is a result of build-up of related and unrelated events.
- Often your stress is more apparent to others than to yourself.
- Reactions to stress can be emotional, physical and behavioural.

Tackling the problem

MANAGING YOUR STRESS
Write down all the signs and symptoms of your stress. Make three lists: things that you can change, those that will improve with time and those about which you can do nothing.

The difficult thing about stress is recognising it; doing something about it is relatively easy. Once you have recognised that you are suffering a stress response, you should be able to identify and tackle any underlying causes, not just the symptoms. And you can ask someone you trust and respect to help.

KEEPING A RECORD

First of all, list all your signs of stress, noting how severe they are and for how long they have lasted. Next, list all the possible causes you can think of, and sort them into categories. Remember that a series of minor irritations may be more distressing than some of the major problems in life.

Having written down all the possible causes of your stress, you can sort them into those that have a practical solution, those that will get better anyway, given time, and those that you can do nothing to change. You should try to let go of those that fall into the second and third groups – try to stop worrying about what you cannot change. Your teenage daughter may give up her attempts to be a model and go back to college, or she may be so successful she becomes a millionairess. The drilling outside may be a distant memory in a month's time. Where there *are* practical solutions (and this applies to most problems), make a list of them and try them out to see if they improve the situation.

You should be prepared for the fact that some of these practical solutions may upset people. Remember that looking after yourself does not mean being unkind to others and that you are most useful to yourself and to others if you are functioning well.

MONITORING PROGRESS

The next stage is to monitor your stress response by keeping a note or brief diary of the changes in the nature, severity or duration of the signs. After a week repeat the process to see how you are getting on: if some of the solutions do not seem to be working, try alternative ones.

Keep assessing progress until you feel that you have reduced as many of the causes of stress as possible and that you are in control of things. Almost certainly things will have vastly improved over 6 to 12 weeks.

In particular, you need to consider four aspects of any persistent unhelpful thoughts:

- How do they relate to the facts?
- What are the alternative interpretations?
- What are the pros and cons of thinking this way?
- Are you jumping to conclusions or blaming yourself unnecessarily?

GROWING UP
The teenage years are a fraught time for both the young adolescent and the family. Most problems sort themselves out with time.

Sample Stress Diary

Make time to keep a stress diary and review the situation every week. Through this exercise you will find it easier not only to monitor your stress levels but also to consider remedies to control them.

STRESS SIGN	SEVERITY (OUT OF 10)	DURATION
AT START DATE		
Sleeplessness	I often lie awake for hours (9/10)	Past 6 weeks
Feeling under pressure	I dread going to work in the morning (7/10)	At least 3 months
Racing heart	Sometimes I feel faint (5/10)	Past 2 weeks
6 WEEKS LATER		
Sleeplessness	Difficulty sleeping (5/10)	3 nights last week
Feeling under pressure	Feel better about going to work if I stop for breakfast in a nearby cafe (3/10)	–
Racing heart	Not too bad last week (1/10)	–
12 WEEKS LATER		
Sleeplessness	Better since altered bedtime routine and exercising regularly (2/10)	–
Feeling under pressure	Got to consider my next career move – decide whether this is the right time (1/10)	–
Racing heart	Better with breathing exercises and relaxation tape (1/10)	–

Causes of Stress and Possible Solutions

You will find it easier to deal with stress if you know what is causing it. Make a list of the causes of your stress, and combine it with a list of possible solutions you intend to put into action.

CATEGORY	CAUSE OF STRESS	POSSIBLE SOLUTION(S)
Family and friends	My mother has had a bad fall	You cannot change what has happened; ensure that the family helps her
	My daughter has dropped out of college	She knows her own mind, and in time you will accept the situation
	I feel I am being left out	The solution is in your hands: get involved in family, clubs, sport, voluntary work, local politics, education
Work	I am pushing myself too hard	There are practical steps that you can take to improve the situation: structure your time, delegate more, give yourself time to think, prioritise activities, have proper breaks during the day, discuss workload with boss/colleagues and reorganise tasks to achieve a balance
	Year-end deadlines	They will pass and so will your stress
Leisure interests	I spend all my spare time watching telly	It is up to you to develop a wider range of interests: arts, sport, films, concerts, theatre
Finances	Credit card account	Stop using it or only use for essentials
Health, appearance and home environment	I am getting old	Accept the situation, and grow old gracefully
	My husband is taking a long time re-decorating	Be patient – he will finish eventually, and you can speed things up by helping him

CONTROLLING YOUR LIFESTYLE

Too much to do and too much responsibility? To avoid feeling overwhelmed you can divide chores into what you 'must' do, what you 'should' do and what you 'needn't' do? The following points may help you to feel more in control of your life:

- Plan a daily or a weekly timetable of activities. Include something new or different each day.
- Plan for the future, and do not dwell on past mistakes or disappointments.
- Cut down on smoking, alcohol, and caffeinated drinks; exercise regularly; eat proper meals; get enough sleep.
- Find time for rest and relaxation.
- Involve family and friends in changing your lifestyle.

CHANGING YOUR THINKING

In order to change the way you think, you need to:

- Think about your thinking. Reward your successes and challenge your criticisms.
- Look out for – and record – unhelpful thoughts that pop into your mind without any effort on your part, that do not fit the facts, that you don't question and are difficult to switch off. Record also your responses to them. Write down as much as possible to begin with. Fast, effective responses will become easier with practice.
- Learn to recognise unhelpful ways of thinking and substitute more realistic and helpful thoughts. By regular practice this will become easier. Start off by writing your thoughts down until you get the hang of it.
- Resist the temptation to avoid thinking about unhelpful thoughts but beware of making excuses – ignoring the problem will not make it go away. The following tips may help you to avoid unhelpful thoughts:

1. Count up how many unhelpful thoughts you have each day and how much time was taken up with these thoughts. For example, you might feel that you have to put up with a shoddy repair job at home because you feel you wouldn't know what to say if you tried to complain. Alternatively, perhaps you might feel that a meeting went badly at work because you are not up to your job.
2. Look for a pattern emerging: if something leads to more unhelpful thoughts, AVOID IT; if something leads to fewer unhelpful thoughts, DO MORE OF IT.
3. Use unhelpful thoughts as a cue for action. Write them down as they occur in a daily diary.

Ways in Which You Can Help Yourself

This chart gives various suggestions of ways to deal with your stress levels through better organisation of time. Do not expect immediate results – allow 2–3 months for the full benefit.

- Write down your hourly timetable. For each activity score 0 to 10 for the pleasure it gives you and 0 to 10 for how well you carry it out. Keep a check on your progress every few days.
- Make a list of what you need to do.
- Plan your timetable to do things that need to be done, do things that give you more pleasure and do things that you can do well.
- Concentrate on goals that are achievable all at once or in small steps.
- Check for unhelpful patterns of thinking, such as: 'I can't cope with this'; 'I've got to get out of this'. How true are these thoughts? If possible, find other ways of thinking about the situation.
- Write down the problem(s) and all the possible options for change, and then try them out, beginning with the most achievable.

ANALYSING YOUR THINKING

Thinking about thinking is not something we usually do, and you may find it difficult at first. It is difficult to think of alternative solutions and different options when you feel stressed.

Just write down what is troubling you, and return to it when you feel more at ease. There is no right answer; look for solutions that help you be more positive.

When every movement seems an effort, the best response can be to make yourself do more.

BENEFITTING FROM ACTIVITIES

Any activity is positive; it:

- Makes you feel better. Activity distracts you, it gives you a sense of control over your life, achievement and pleasure;
- Gives you the strength and stamina to feel less tired;
- Helps you become motivated. The more you do the more you want to do;
- Helps you think straight;
- Pleases and impresses those around you.

Make yourself an activity plan in the form of an hourly timetable of what you do, based on the following schedule.

MAKING AN ACTIVITY SCHEDULE

An activity schedule gives you information about what you are doing now and what more you can do in the future. It confirms that you are not 'doing nothing'.

For three days record exactly what you do hour by hour. Give each of your activities a rating between 0 and 10 for enjoyment (E), pleasure (P), achievement (A) and mastery (M), with 10 being the most rewarding and 0 the least.

E10 means that the activity was highly enjoyable and A10 means there was a high sense of achievement. Make the ratings at the time of the activity and not in retrospect, and relate them to you as you are now and not how you once were at some perfect time in the past.

PLANNING ACTIVITIES

What would you like to improve? How can you change things for the better?

Plan each day in advance, including activities that give you enjoyment and a sense of achievement:

- Structuring time allows you to feel that you are gaining control and have a sense of purpose.
- A daily or weekly framework provides meaningful structure for living.
- Once the day or the week's activities are planned and structured they are broken down into a series of manageable units that are less overwhelming.

MAKING THE MOST OF ACTIVITIES

- Be flexible, not a slave to routine.
- Think of alternatives – you can't picnic when it rains.
- Keep to the plan. If you have some 'free time', fill it in with something from a list of pleasurable activities you keep handy.
- Schedule activities by the half hour or hour.
- Concentrate on how much time you are going to spend, not how much you are going to do in the time available. You weed for an hour, not to collect a hundredweight of weeds.
- Work to the schedule. Work steadily to gain results.
- Review the situation. What have you enjoyed achieving?

Dealing with Unhelpful Thoughts

Ask yourself each of the following questions. Your answers will help you to recognise and challenge any unhelpful thoughts that may be hindering your life, and find a way of dealing with them.

- Is the problem a thought or is it a fact?
- Am I jumping to conclusions?
- What is the alternative?
- What is the effect on me of thinking this way?
- What are the advantages and disadvantages?
- Is there any answer to this?
- Am I thinking in black-and-white terms?
- Are the issues really as clear cut as 'always versus never' and 'everything versus nothing'?
- Is everything wrong because of one event or change?
- Are my weaknesses overshadowing my strengths?
- How appropriate is blame?
- How much of this is to do with me?
- How perfect can I be?
- Have I got double standards?
- Is there only a down side?
- Is everything likely to be a disaster?
- Are things out of proportion?
- Am I living life the way it is or the way I'd wish it to be?
- Isn't there anything that can change?
- What can I do to affect the outcome of this situation?

Sample Problems and Possible Solutions

Write down all the problems you experience during the course of each day. If you then list ways in which you can combat or solve the problems you are doing something positive to help yourself.

PROBLEMS	SOLUTIONS
I can't cope with having the in-laws to lunch.	If I write down what I need to do, it won't be so overwhelming. I can take the things one at a time. I don't have to do them all at once.
It's too difficult to sort out the muddle at work.	I've done more difficult things than this in the past.
I don't want to go to an exercise class.	I don't now but I did earlier on. It would be better for me to do it. I'll feel good about it afterwards.
I don't think I'm up to making a difficult phone call just now.	I won't know until I try. If I wait till I feel like it, I'll never do it. I'll feel better when I've done it.
I won't be able to do everything I've planned because there simply isn't enough time.	No one does all they've planned. Think about what I have done, not what I haven't.
I can't decide which thing to do first because they're all equally important.	Do the first in alphabetical order. The most important thing is to do something. Once I get started I'll have a clearer idea of what to do next.

GETTING STARTED

Try combating your problems in the following ways:

- Make a list of things you have been putting off, such as getting the car serviced, phoning an awkward relative, cleaning the cooker;
- Number tasks in order of priority, and try to do those with the highest priority. For example, if your car is making odd noises and hasn't been near a garage for months, that job should be near the top of your list.
- Break the first task into small steps: check your diary to see whether you'll be needing the car for something vital; find the phone number of the garage. Ring and book it in.
- When you face a difficult task, rehearse the task in your mind step by step.

GETTING ORGANISED
When faced with a host of tasks, careful planning will help. Prioritise the tasks, and begin with the most important one.

WRITING IT DOWN

Write down any difficulties that you foresee and how to get round them:

- Stop writing while you are still successfully finding solutions; you will feel keener to try again next time.
- When you finish, immediately write down what you have done on your activity schedule, and rate it for enjoyment and achievement.
- Concentrate on achievements.

Don't give up on this process. Remember next time to:

- Go back and look at your priority list again.
- Tackle the next task in the same way.

KEY POINTS

- Once you have recognised that you are suffering a stress response, then you should be able to identify and tackle any underlying causes.
- List your signs of stress.
- List the probable causes of your stress.
- Monitor the changes in the nature, severity or duration of the signs of your stress.
- Look out for unhelpful thoughts, and think of new solutions to them.
- Try your solutions.
- Plans and activities are powerful weapons to overcome stress.

Defences against stress

We can defend ourselves against stress in our lives by understanding what causes us stress, and by learning how to avoid it or adjust and adapt better. The principal defences are within ourselves and mainly consist of physical and mental fitness – a healthy body and a healthy mind.

PHYSICAL DEFENCES

We can improve our defences by leading a healthy, enjoyable life and by looking after ourselves.

SLEEP

First, ensure that you get enough sleep. This can be encouraged by learning how to relax (see tables on pp.41–42). Sleep does 'knit up the ravelled sleeve of care'. The amount needed varies from person to person, but it is probably true to say that more is needed during times of stress than when life is running smoothly. Beware of taking too much sleep – it can make you feel as bad as too little. Sleeping problems are common among those under stress, but do not worry unnecessarily about a few bad nights – you can usually catch up after one good night's sleep.

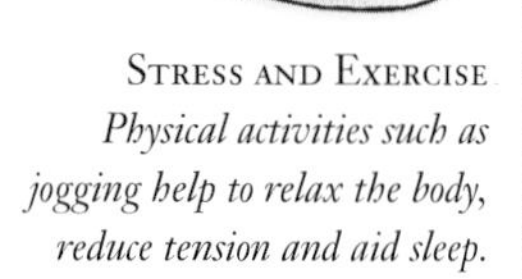

STRESS AND EXERCISE
Physical activities such as jogging help to relax the body, reduce tension and aid sleep.

Beating Insomnia
There are many practical things that you can do to ensure a deep, restful sleep. Tire yourself physically, pay attention to what and when you eat and drink, and take time to relax before retiring to bed.

If you are having difficulty in sleeping, reduce your overall daily consumption of tea, coffee and soft drinks containing caffeine, eat supper early and avoid strong tea or coffee, unless it is decaffeinated, in the afternoon and evening. Try to tire yourself physically by taking some pleasant exercise, for example, a brisk walk or gardening, then have a bath and spend some time switching your mind off before going to bed by reading or watching television or even playing a game of Patience. Do not allow yourself to brood over problems; they can wait until the morning! If you can't get to sleep, or wake in the middle of the night and can't get to sleep again, get up, make yourself a drink (preferably with hot milk, and not tea or coffee), have another game of Patience or do some mindless chore like sorting your sock drawer out or tidying the tool box, and then go back to bed. Do not lie in bed worrying. Try not to take sleeping pills unless it's only for one or two nights in order to break the pattern of sleeplessness. Pills can make you feel fuzzy and dopey in the morning, and even less able to deal with the day ahead. They can also develop into an unwelcome habit which could end up causing you even more stress.

Diet

Try to keep to the ideal weight for your height. We should all eat a sensible diet to avoid the health hazards of being overweight, and to reduce or prevent the risks of developing diseases known to be related to diet, such as heart disease, high blood pressure, bowel cancer and late-onset diabetes.

The main principles are to eat far less fat and fatty foods, especially those containing saturated fats and cholesterol; increase dietary fibre by eating more whole-grain cereals, pulses and fresh fruit and vegetables; cut down on sugar and salt. This can be difficult as it goes against all that many of us hold dear, such as the traditional Sunday lunch of roast beef, Yorkshire pudding and roast potatoes! Don't go too quickly in your campaign for diet reform; change a few

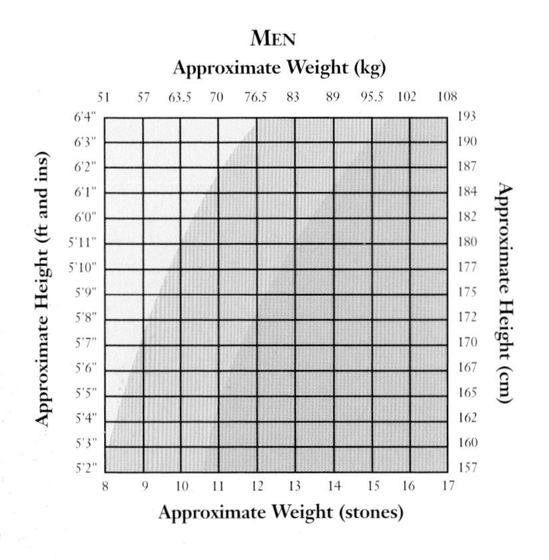

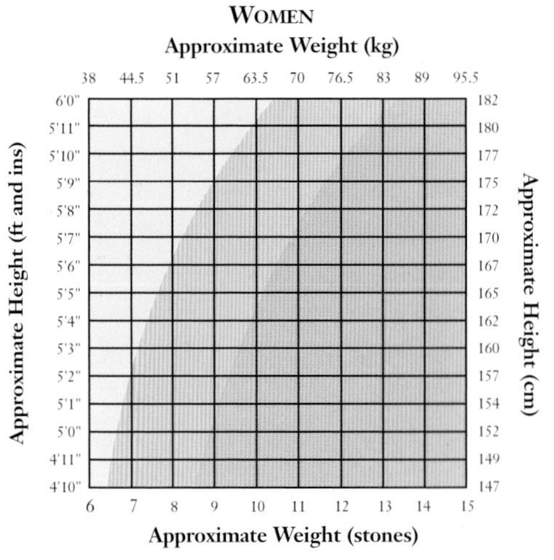

Key:

Underweight **Normal Weight** **Overweight**

Check Your Weight

Try to keep your weight around the level best suited to your height and build.

products at a time, and add new foods rather than just cutting out those that you currently eat and are bad for you. If you live for Sunday roast lunch, don't abandon it completely. Just try to cut back on the fatty bits. Changing your diet should not be a torture – it should be fun!

Be careful about what you drink. Too much tea or coffee can be over-stimulating, and excessive alcohol is certainly no friend to good health. You should also avoid drinks with a lot of sugar or caffeine.

THE BENEFITS OF EXERCISE
Regular exercise such as aerobics will not only keep your body fit and healthy, but will also improve your state of mind. Exercise can be fun – choose an activity that you enjoy.

EXERCISE

There is only one way to keep the body trim and fit – by exercise. We all need some regular exercise, preferably daily. This might amount to no more than a pleasant, brisk 20-minute walk in the fresh air, but it could well be much more. At the very least, you will be more likely to feel physically and mentally relaxed, be able to get a refreshing sleep and your appetite will be stimulated. The important thing is that the exercise chosen should be pleasurable to you – which for some of us can be a problem!

MENTAL DEFENCES

Improving general health and fitness can protect against and lessen the effects of stress. Some events are in themselves stressful, but many of our reactions to these depend on our attitudes, beliefs and values. The mind has a whole series of defence mechanisms, described in the last section of this book, and although these may be helpful in the short term, they may act as a barrier to adapting and coping with stress.

Helping Yourself with Exercise

Whatever you decide to do in the way of exercise, it is important that you always consider – and follow – the points below.

- Warm up for two or three minutes before starting by stretching or running on the spot.
- Build up slowly, and do not over-extend yourself – always exercise within the limits of comfort (let your breathing be your guide), and if it hurts, stop.
- If you feel excessively tired, stop and rest – there is always tomorrow.
- When stopping exercise, cool down gradually and slowly to avoid stiffness.
- Exercise sessions three times a week for about 20 minutes, at a pace that keeps you moderately 'puffed' (not gasping for breath), are likely to be best for stimulating both muscles and circulation.

In overcoming stress we often do not have appropriate or enough coping strategies available. We need to learn new skills of self-instruction and self-control.

SELF-INSTRUCTION

When we learn a new skill, such as driving a car, we learn from a combination of observation and instruction. At the beginning, we are usually instructed by someone else; then we repeat the process, giving the instructions to ourselves; finally, once we have learned the skills, we are able to drive 'automatically' without consciously thinking of what we are doing. We can apply a similar process to our everyday thinking:

- observation;
- instruction;
- self-instruction;
- automatic ability.

For example, suppose we feel stressed about taking examinations or having job interviews. First, using a little imagination before the event, we can pay attention to the way our thoughts tend to work when the stress is imminent. What are the things that we say to ourselves? Perhaps 'Oh, my God, what can I say?'; 'I wish this was all over'; 'I wish I hadn't started this'; 'Two hours still to go'; 'They must think I'm an idiot'; and so on.

Next, we can make a list of positive, practical instructions that would be more useful. Such as 'I had better start writing' rather than 'I'm very nervous'; or 'These are the main points and these are things I want to emphasise' rather than 'I don't know what they're looking for'.

Third, during the event, we instruct ourselves positively with the most useful instructions we have thought of beforehand, instead of wasting time and energy panicking or ruminating on irrelevant thoughts. In time this process becomes 'automatic'.

SELF-CONTROL

Having a sense of control over events lessens their stressful impact. True, there are some things over which we have no control, but there is usually some aspect of a problem that we can change to our advantage, thereby reducing stressful feelings of helplessness.

Self-control methods can be very useful when we wish to alter particular aspects of our behaviour or response to people or events.

First, carefully observe the behaviour in question, for example, always getting angry with Bloggins at work, or being irritable with the family at breakfast time or regularly missing the bus/train because you leave home too late. Chart the circumstances in a diary made up for the purpose.

Now, think of practical ways in which you can modify the behaviour. For example, take a deep breath and ask Bloggins if you can help him. Make a point of saying something nice at breakfast. Make sure you leave home in plenty of time to catch the bus/train.

The next part of the process of self-control involves reward. Choose something pleasant with which to reward yourself when you change the behaviour in question and reach a certain predetermined standard – buy yourself a treat if you manage to catch your bus/train every morning for a whole week without rushing!

RELAXATION

Relaxation is a useful technique to practise when you feel under stress. There are a number of similar methods, but one of the most widely used is described on p.42. Read the instructions, and familiarise yourself with them before having a go. You may be able to borrow a 'relaxation tape' from your general practice or local library. Do be patient, and give yourself several tries before expecting the full beneficial results – for those of us who are very 'twitchy' it can take time to learn to relax.

To begin with practise for 30 minutes three or four times a day, then slowly reduce the 'dose' to once a day as you feel better. If you feel under stress again, increase the dose!

The Advantages of Regular Relaxation

- Improves sleep
- Increases mental and physical performance
- Combats tiredness
- Decreases anxiety and tension
- Is not addictive

Preparing for Relaxation

Before starting on any relaxation routine, it is important to ensure that your mind, body and environment are properly prepared. The following steps are a guide to such preparation.

- Sit in a comfortable chair or (even better) lie down somewhere comfortable in a quiet, warm room where you will not be interrupted.
- If you are sitting, take off your shoes, uncross your legs and rest your arms on the arms of the chair.
- If you are lying down, lie on your back with your arms at your side. If necessary, use a comfortable pillow for your head.
- Close your eyes, and be aware of your body. Notice how you are breathing and where the muscular tensions are. Make sure you are comfortable.

Breathing to Relax

In order to achieve relaxation it is essential that you use the correct breathing technique. Follow the steps below, and perfect your breathing method before starting the relaxation sequence (p.42).

- Drop your jaw and shoulders. Breathe slowly and deeply, in through your nose and out through your mouth, expanding your abdomen as you breathe in. Raise your rib cage to let more air in, filling your lungs to the top.
- Hold your breath for three to six seconds and breathe out slowly, allowing your rib cage and stomach to relax, and empty your lungs completely.
- Do not strain – with practice it will become much easier.
- Keep this slow, deep, rhythmic breathing going throughout your relaxation session.
- Remember to breathe deeply and be aware when you relax of the feeling of physical well-being and heaviness spreading through your body.

Using and Adapting a Relaxation Sequence

First establish a breathing pattern (see p.41). Then follow these guidelines: inhale as you carry out each step below, hold the breath and the position for 10 seconds, relax and exhale, move to the next step.

1 Lie down. Curl your toes hard, and press your feet down.

2 Press your heels down, and bend your feet up.

3 Tense your calf muscles.

4 Tense your thigh muscles, straightening your knees and making your legs stiff.

5 Make your buttocks tight.

6 Tense your stomach as if to receive a punch.

7 Bend your elbows, and tense the muscles of your arms.

8 Hunch your shoulders, and press your head back into the cushion or pillow.

9 Clench your jaws, frown and screw up your eyes really tight.

10 Tense all your muscles together.

11 After 10 seconds, relax completely.

12 Close your eyes.

13 Continue to breathe slowly and deeply, imagine a white rose on a black background. Try to 'see' the rose as clearly as possible, concentrating your attention on it for 30 seconds. Do not hold your breath during this time; continue to breathe as you have been doing.

14 Repeat step 13, visualising another peaceful object of your own choice.

15 Lastly, give yourself the instruction that, when you open your eyes, you will be perfectly relaxed and alert.

16 Open your eyes.

17 Repeat steps 1–16 five to ten times.

Once familiar with this technique, you can use it even if you have just a few minutes by leaving out some muscle groups – but always work from the feet upwards. For example, you may do steps 1, 4, 6, 8 and 10.

PUTTING IT ALL TOGETHER

Bring together the stress management techniques for day-to-day use through combining the monitoring of physical and mental signs of stress, use of self-instruction, deep breathing and relaxation as a means of rapid stress control.

For example, stick a red dot at the centre of your watch as a regular reminder to practise monitoring physical tension and any thoughts which might be causing stress during the day. Practise challenging thoughts (tell yourself 'stop getting worked up') or, at a minimum, ease yourself into relaxing by saying 'relax', and do this by taking a slow, deep breath, holding it for three to six seconds and letting it out slowly while practising your relaxation technique at the same time.

KEY POINTS

- We can defend against stress by understanding its causes.
- The principal defences against stress are physical and mental fitness.
- Physical fitness is improved by healthy lifestyle, adequate sleep, eating a balanced diet and taking regular exercise.
- Our mental fitness to deal with stress is helped by self-instruction and self-control.
- Relaxation techniques are useful when you feel stressed.

How to help yourself

Many people find their own ways of tackling stress without needing the help of doctors or other health professionals.

The main questions to ask yourself are:

- 'Is there anything I can do when I feel stressed that makes me feel better?' If so, keep doing it – except in the case of 'false friends' (see pp.72–80).
- 'Is there anything I do that makes me feel worse?' In general, avoid it if you can.
- 'Is there anything that I think might help if only I could do it?' Try it out if this is at all possible.

Tackling Problems

In addition to looking after yourself, adopting a problem-solving approach can help you to find exactly what the stress is and to devise a plan to cope with it. Even though some stresses cannot be fully resolved in this way, you will usually find that you're more able to cope, so that the overall impact of stress is reduced.

Controlling Stress
Keep yourself occupied with pleasurable activities such as shopping, and turn to friends for support and encouragement.

Rejecting Unpleasant Thoughts

Miserable feelings and unpleasant thoughts tend to focus your attention on aspects that you do not like about yourself or your life. They tend to exaggerate problems so that they seem overwhelming and make you feel worse. Although it may be difficult to distract yourself from unpleasant thoughts, it does help to decide not to think about them and fill your mind with something else. This can be done by a combination of:

- Concentrating on events around you such as other conversations, the number of blue things you can see, in fact anything that holds your attention;
- Any absorbing mental activity you enjoy, such as mental arithmetic, games and puzzles, crosswords, reading;
- Any physical activity that keeps you occupied, such as going for a walk, doing housework or taking a trip.

Asking Friends to Help

Unpleasant thoughts make you tend to underestimate your positive characteristics and ability to solve problems. A number of strategies may help you achieve a more balanced view of things. Recruit a friend or relative to help you see things more clearly:

- Make a list of your three best attributes with the help of a trusted friend or close relative. Perhaps people would describe you, for example, as generous, affectionate and reliable.
- Carry the list with you, and read it three times whenever you think unpleasant thoughts.
- Keep a daily diary of all the small, pleasant events that happen and talk about them with a friend each day.
- Recall pleasant occasions in the past and plan pleasant ones for the future, again with a friend if possible.

How to Deal with the Effects of Stress

If you are experiencing symptoms of stress or know that you are going to be in a stressful situation, you can minimise many of the physical effects by utilising these simple self-help techniques.

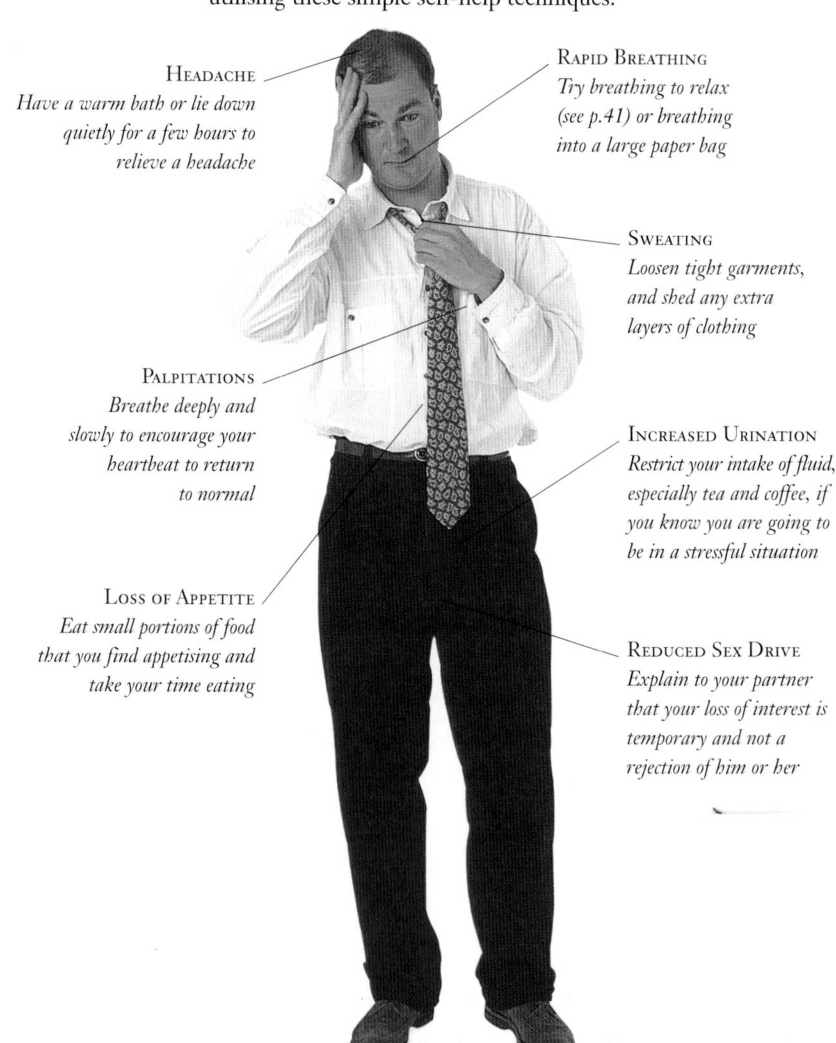

- Avoid talking about your unpleasant thoughts – expressing unreasonable thoughts about yourself is extremely negative and unhelpful; tackling your real problems is much more constructive.
- If you start airing negative thoughts about yourself, ask friends to interrupt politely and focus on positive ideas.
- Always consider alternative explanations for any unpleasant events or thoughts rather than automatically blaming yourself.
- Keep your mind occupied by planning and doing constructive tasks – avoid sitting or lying around daydreaming or doing nothing.

Stress is almost always accompanied by symptoms of anxiety, tension or nervousness, such as muscle tension, trembling, cold sweats, butterflies in the stomach, rapid or difficult shallow breathing, and a rapid or irregular pounding heartbeat. This response may be triggered off by situations such as an enclosed space, a crowded supermarket or even meeting a friend. At other times unpleasant thoughts, for example, of dying or failure at work, may trigger off feelings of anxiety and panic.

Why the Panic?

It's almost always possible to identify situations or thoughts that trigger off panic. Remember that anxiety is not harmful and always goes away after a time:

- Wait, and the feelings will pass.
- Practise a routine to use whenever you sense panicky feelings starting.
- It can be helpful to start by taking a deep breath and then slowing down and deepening your breathing pattern.
- Try to distract yourself by concentrating on something pleasant as this will stop you adding to the panic.

- As the panicky feeling subsides, plan something pleasant to do next.

Dealing with Loss of Appetite

- Eat small portions of foods that you find particularly appetising and appealing.
- Take your time eating.
- Temporarily avoid situations that make you feel under pressure to finish eating.
- Drink plenty of fluids, especially water and fruit juices.

Weight loss may be an important indicator of the extent of stress, so if you continue to lose weight, see your GP.

Dealing with Loss of Sexual Drive

Decreased interest in sex is frequently a feature of stress and is a cause of much distress. It won't last forever, but in the meantime, try to enjoy those aspects of your sexual relationship that are still a pleasure. You should explain to your partner that your loss of interest and affection is a temporary symptom of your condition and should not be considered a rejection of him or her.

If your interest shows no sign of reviving within a few weeks, discuss the problems with your GP or another professional adviser or confidant. Things can improve with help.

Putting Worry Behind You

Worry is a pretty pointless activity and never solved anything, so here are three plans to counter it:

Solving Problems

Put your worrying to constructive use. Rather than endlessly pinpointing your problems, pick out one or two that seem really important, and make specific plans to resolve them (you may find it helpful to do this with a friend). Sit down with a sheet of paper and pencil, and go through the following steps making notes as you go:

- Write down exactly what the problem is.
- List five or six possible solutions to the problem – write down any ideas that occur to you, not merely 'good' ideas.
- Weigh up the good and bad points of each idea.
- Choose the solution that best fits your needs.
- Plan the steps you must take to achieve the solution.
- Reassess your efforts after attempting to carry out your plan (remember to praise all your efforts).
- If you are unsuccessful start again – this time trying a new plan.

Rethinking an Unpleasant Experience

- List every feature of the experience, 'I'm sweating . . . the hairs on my arm are standing on end . . . my heart is pounding hard . . . I think I'm going to scream . . . my legs feel like jelly . . . I'm going to pass out'. Write these down on a card.
- Talk yourself into staying with these unpleasant feelings. Tell yourself exactly how you feel, and remind yourself that the feelings will reach a peak and then start to get better.
- Re-label your experiences: imagine that you are playing an energetic sport in an intimidating environment – a cup final or a singles final at Wimbledon – and that this accounts for your pounding heart, rapid breathing and feelings of excitement.
- Think catastrophic thoughts, focusing your mind on the worst possible thing that could happen to you, for example,

collapsing, screaming, throwing your clothes off, being sick or incontinent, etc. Plan exactly what you would do if it did actually happen. Next time it will be a little easier to cope with the feelings, and with practice and monitoring you will find that you are beginning to control and overcome worry.

Keeping a Stress Diary

A stress diary is an important part of helping to deal with stress. Follow the advice given here.

- Write down what happens each day.
- Score yourself from 0 to 10 (best) for each day or week..
- Write down all your successes, large or small.
- Write down what self-help technique you were using, what target you were trying to achieve and whether you were practising it regularly.
- Write down what you did not avoid thinking about or doing.
- Write down what you did for enjoyment or fun.
- Look back at your diary every week to see what progress you have made and to plan what you intend to achieve next week.

RELAXING

- Take an interest.
- Set some goals for your daily activities: for example, I will get up by 9 a.m., meet a friend, read an article in the newspaper.
- In small steps, build a full programme of constructive activities for the day.
- Avoid comparing your current levels of performance and interests with those in the past – concentrate on the here and now and on the future.
- If a task seems too difficult, do not despair. Break it down into even easier steps, and start again more slowly.
- Above all, reward yourself for your efforts.
- Try to have others around you to encourage and praise you for every small step you take.

OVERCOMING SETBACKS

Everyone has setbacks from day to day. These are to be expected, and you should try to keep your mind on your long-term goals:

- Try to approach the problem in a different way.
- Try to approach the difficulty in smaller steps or stages.
- Try to continue practising because eventually this will help you overcome your difficulties.
- Remember that you will probably be more successful if you can make your activities or rewards as enjoyable as possible.

It is common to think that you are not making any progress to begin with and to underrate your achievements. It's a good idea to have a member of the family or a friend to give you an independent opinion about your progress and to offer encouragement.

A simple daily or weekly record or diary will help you keep track of improvement. The first signs are usually quite small, sometimes hardly noticeable, but writing everything down will help you see exactly what has happened. Don't just rely on your memory: people have a tendency to remember setbacks more than successes. Again, it is helpful to involve someone else in assessing your improvement to give an independent opinion.

KEY POINTS

- Many people find their own ways of tackling stress.
- Anxiety attacks always go away after a time.
- Worry is a pointless activity and never solved anything.
- Confront your problems, and make plans to solve them.
- Everybody has setbacks – and they can be overcome.

Getting help

Coping with stress can be made easier by having some support and help from family and friends. In fact, not having any family or friends to call on may itself create or worsen stress.

FAMILY SUPPORT
Turn to your family for help. Problems will seem less over-powering if they are shared with a sympathetic listener.

For example, if you are feeling anxious or uncertain about some event that has recently happened, such as getting into debt or worrying that you might be going to lose your job, your stress may be increased by not having anyone to talk to about your fears. You may easily believe that other people don't worry in the same way, that there is no way you can escape from the pressure and that no one else is interested. You could be convinced that no one else will understand or has ever experienced similar anxieties about such a common event, and that the fact that you are having difficulty in coping is a sign of weakness and something to be ashamed of and hidden.

Good friends and loving relationships help to counteract stress. Support can be found simply in having a stable home life or a trouble-free atmosphere at work.

Such a refuge can provide breathing space, enabling us to work our way through and sort out a particularly stressful problem for ourselves and in our own time.

It is an enormous help if you have someone to talk to who will listen sympathetically and in confidence and who will, if you want, provide moral support, practical advice, company or simply be there to take your mind off your problems.

Talking to someone helps you to see a problem more clearly, to get things in proportion, to explore all the possible answers and to face up to, and learn to get through, the causes of your stress.

FEELING ALONE

Many people, unfortunately, do not (or think that they do not) have any close family or good friends to turn to for help. Loneliness and isolation may be difficult to escape from; fear of rejection may put you off trying to make new friends. But the important thing is to recognise the need for outside help, and not to see this as a failure and something of which to be ashamed. If you already have a large family and/or a social network of friends, then you will need to learn how to benefit from them in coping with your high levels of stress.

If, on the other hand, feelings of isolation are a major part of the problem, you could try to develop a social network by offering friendship and support to others and receiving it from them in return. You will benefit from making the effort to find new friends and stimulation through, for example, taking up evening classes, courses, sports, voluntary work or political activities.

FEELING LONELY?
Loneliness may be a cause of stress in itself. If you feel that you have no close friends or family, try to widen your social network with new activities.

None of these steps is easy, and they all involve making a conscious effort to look outward, to be open and receptive to other people, and optimistic and resilient in the face of difficulties, but they can, in time, be extremely beneficial and rewarding. Try not to forget that there are other people feeling just as isolated and with just as much potential for giving as yourself: to find them you must come out of yourself.

SEEKING HELP

If you are not coping with stress, get help as soon as possible – the earlier help starts the better. You may find that the very act of seeking help and discussing problems with your family and friends gives immediate relief.

SHARING PROBLEMS
Talking to people with similar problems and feelings can be of great benefit, helping to reduce stress and negative feelings.

There are three main types of help available: medical, psychological and social. In practice these elements are often combined in the various treatment packages offered by different professionals – except that prescriptions for medication can only be written by medical doctors. GPs, social workers, clinical psychologists, community psychiatric nurses, counsellors and psychiatrists have important roles to play. The personal qualities of such people are important and should include acceptance, warmth, genuineness, empathy, a tolerant attitude, dependability, continuity and an interest that allows them to take even seemingly minor problems seriously.

YOUR GP

For many people under stress, particularly those with no or few confidants, the family doctor becomes the first and the chief source of help. Doctors are trained to deal with all aspects of life that affect health but, like other people, they vary in their reaction to the stress responses they have to help with.

Most GPs prefer to deal with stress by counselling and general advice. Even the act of giving a full account of the circumstances surrounding the stress, with the doctor listening carefully to the descriptions, is usually beneficial because it helps to get the stress in perspective, so that adjustments and decisions can be made.

The doctor may perform a thorough examination and, in a few cases, arrange for special blood tests. The signs of stress may seem overwhelming to you and appear to mean disease, and it is reassuring to find out that no serious disease is present and that the body is functioning perfectly efficiently, even under stress. Whatever the outcome, an appointment with the GP is an opportunity to discuss ways of reducing stress as well as where help and further information can be obtained.

MENTAL HEALTH SERVICES IN THE NHS

For most people the first professional contact is their GP. Access to specialist help from community psychiatric nurses, psychiatrists, clinical psychologists, psychotherapists and others in the NHS can often only be obtained through your GP. Occasionally specialists will agree to see you without a GP referral, but they usually want to keep your GP aware of their involvement. If you want to see a specialist, but for some reason cannot get a referral, it is worth getting in touch with your local hospital to find out if you can be seen by self-referral.

Mental health services, like others within the NHS, are under severe pressure. Most people are treated by their GP, and if they are referred to a hospital specialist it can take some time before they are seen.

PRIVATE SPECIALISTS

You can see a psychiatrist or other mental health specialist privately. This can be arranged by your GP or by getting in touch with a local private psychiatric hospital or clinic.

SELF-REFERRAL AGENCIES

Because of pressure on hospital services and criticism of the traditional medical approach, there are an increasing number of voluntary and private self-referral agencies. Details are usually available from your local community health council, Citizen's Advice Bureau, social services department, library or community centre.

If, as well as loneliness and isolation, some more serious or specific difficulty is involved, then the various caring agencies can also provide support on a temporary or long-term basis. There are also a number of national organisations that offer help, advice and information about particular conditions or problems, and they will be able to give you further details about local facilities.

Notice boards in local libraries are often a good source of information about local helping agencies and facilities. Your library should have access to a copy of the Mental Health Foundation's 'Someone to Talk To' directory or a similar guide, which lists all these groups.

The essential thing is to try to identify the source of stress in your life, decide what kind of help you think would be best for you and seek help from the people or agencies that you feel most comfortable about approaching. Also, try to recognise that, like you, the people you turn to will have different strengths and weaknesses, and if you feel that a particular approach is not working, say so, and see if it can be changed, or (preferably by mutual agreement) try elsewhere. Do not be deterred if your first approach does not bring an instant solution – keep trying.

SEEKING PROFESIONAL HELP
Counsellors, GPs, nurses or psychologists will be able to offer practical advice on how to set about reducing the stress factors in your life.

OTHER TYPES OF HELP

The traditional medical approach to treatment has been criticised for being too narrow and neglecting personal and social aspects. Because of this critisism a variety of psychological approaches has been developed for use in addition to medical treatment or alone.

VOLUNTARY BODIES

Voluntary bodies such as The Samaritans can provide a sympathetic ear, information and advice. Your local health authority has a health information service and contact numbers for other local voluntary groups. Where relationship problems are causing the majority of your problems, it may be useful to contact your local branch of Relate (see Useful Addresses, pp.90–91).

MINISTERS OF RELIGION

For many stressed people, there is a natural tendency to turn to religion for spiritual solace and support. For those who have religious faith, the strength of shared belief and the sense of belonging and common purpose with like-minded people can overcome adversity and demoralisation. Ministers of religion usually have great experience in counselling and are often more than willing to talk things over and provide support.

SUPPORT & COUNSELLING

Most GPs and health professionals often find themselves in the position of giving emotional support, advice and counselling in an effort to provide reassurance, encouragement and sympathy. Indeed this is probably the most common and most successful help. In many cases, listening may be more important than giving advice – provided that listening means not only hearing the words spoken but also taking note of what the person is saying and trying to understand how she or he feels.

- Your counsellor should allow you to express appropriate emotions and reassure you that they are perfectly 'normal'; a hand on the shoulder may do more good than any number of words.

TALKING TO A COUNSELLOR
A counsellor will encourage you to explain your problems and express your feelings.

- Any irrational anger and guilt you feel are accepted and not discounted.
- You can talk through events leading up to a crisis.
- You can test the reality of events described.
- You can explore the implications.
- You may find encouragement to seek new directions in life.

But beware of seeing problems as entirely due to stress and likewise of becoming too dependent on professional helpers and counsellors.

WHAT IS COUNSELLING?

Counselling is the name given to a range of activities in which an attempt is made to understand the effects of some event on an individual or family, and to plan, with the person or people concerned, how to manage the emotional and practical realities. The purpose is not to impose an answer, but to assist the person to live the life he or she has consciously chosen.

As almost anyone can set themselves up as a counsellor, it is wise to ensure beforehand that the person you choose is trained, qualified and experienced. You can do this by asking for advice from your doctor or one of the self-help agencies. Also, a list of qualified counsellors can be obtained by sending a self-addressed envelope to the British Association for Counselling (see p.90).

There are many different counselling techniques, but the main characteristics of a successful counsellor are emotional warmth, understanding and genuineness. You also need to feel that he or she is someone you can relate to. Counselling usually takes place regularly over a period of weeks or a few months.

REASSURANCE

This is still probably the most widely used form of counselling. Bland reassurance is seldom, if ever, useful, but careful listening will help identify the main stress, and then reassurance can consist of 'new' information which is relevant to reducing the stress, put in a form that is easy to understand and remember.

BEHAVIOURAL COUNSELLING

Behavioural counselling aims to change behaviour. The main concern is to relieve a specific difficulty or symptom by studying the patterns of behaviour that led to difficulty, and then modifying responses by learning more useful ways of dealing with problems. The accent is on 'doing' rather than just 'talking'. People who have difficulties with relationships (for example, shyness or embarrassment) can learn useful new 'social skills' in this way. After discussing and observing your behaviour, the counsellor or therapist may first explain the effects of this on other people, perhaps using a videotape to show you how you function. When you have together identified the problems in your approach, the therapist may then coach you in new, more effective ways of behaving, and get you to act them out in a 'role play' with other people. Alternatively, the therapist may ask you to take on the role of someone with whom you have particular difficulties, to help you to see clearly and from a different angle how your own responses work.

RATIONAL-EMOTIVE COUNSELLING

Rational-emotive counselling considers the way in which we 'worry about being worried'. This type of counselling involves identifying the irrational ways in which we think about problems, and then helps us find less stress-provoking ways of dealing with them.

ROGERIAN COUNSELLING

This is based not on telling us what to do, but on helping us work out for ourselves what we want and how best to achieve it. The counsellor facilitates self-understanding by 'mirroring-back' to us our own understanding, to help us to re-shape our thoughts and feelings, to share our experiences and to discuss their development with us.

HUMANISTIC COUNSELLING

This is concerned with 'personal growth' and helping us to achieve our full potential. Workers in this form of counselling make use of encounter groups and personal therapy, massage, meditation, dancing, co-counselling and virtually any method that seems likely to help people under stress to understand themselves more clearly and to feel better. This technique's aim is to integrate the health and well-being of the person as a whole.

USING MEDITATION
Humanistic counsellors encourage techniques such as meditation to release tension and recharge both body and mind.

UNDERGOING PSYCHOTHERAPY
Through one-to-one contact with patients, a psychotherapist can help those whose stress has its roots in their particular life experiences or personalities.

PSYCHOTHERAPY

Any treatment that does not use drugs or other physical methods could be called psychotherapy. The single most important element of psychotherapy is talking, and it is the ideas behind the therapy, the way it is applied and the nature of the relationships that develop between the person and the therapist which differentiate the various types of psychotherapy practice.

Some schools of therapy emphasise the importance of loss (for example, of loved ones, objects or cherished ideas), others propose that we humans have an inborn tendency to seek attachments with others that build emotional and social bonds and lead to experiences of warmth, nurturing and protection. Destruction of these close bonds may make people especially vulnerable to stress.

The concept of attachment bonds provides a basis for understanding development of personality and for developing strategies to correct distortions produced by faulty or inadequate attachments in childhood.

Strong attachment bonds seem to be especially important and valuable when people are faced with situations causing adversity and stress.

Depending on the approach taken by the psychotherapist, you may be helped to express and redirect anger and hostility in more appropriate ways, or you may work together to examine current personal relationships and to understand how they have developed from experiences with attachment figures in childhood, adolescence and adulthood.

The psychotherapeutic approach to treatment has arisen out of various theories which view disturbances in personal relationships as contributing to stress and depression. Particularly important are relationship difficulties such as:

- Loss or bereavement;
- Disputes about roles (specially those of husband/wife);
- Role transitions (becoming a mother, divorce);
- Lack of close, confiding relationships.

In essence, psychotherapeutic treatment is concerned with identifying problems in your closest relationships and in considering alternative ways of behaving and thinking.

The discussion between the person and the therapist concentrates on:

- Emotions generated by close relationships (including warmth, anger, trust, envy, jealousy);
- Family relationships;
- Friendship patterns;
- Work;
- Attitudes to neighbourhood and community.

Many people assume that one or other variety of psychotherapy would suit them and their individual problems. Psychotherapy, especially psychoanalysis, which may last years, is often prolonged, intensive and expensive. In addition it is not easily available throughout the country. It is very difficult to judge its benefits, whether it is given individually or in groups. For these reasons, and because it is possible for some individuals to feel worse and more stressed after psychotherapy, it may be considered inappropriate for some people.

CHANGING YOUR THINKING

Your therapist may he[illegible] you choose actio[illegible]s which are likely to change unhe[illegible]pful ways of thinking [illegible] arning from experience'. It is not enough simply to help you change the content of a particular thought; it is essential that you should recognise and change the reasoning process that led you to a false conclusion if you are to avoid making similar errors in the future.

Although the 'cognitive' therapist pays particular attention to the intrusive unhelpful thoughts that precede the change of mood or feeling of stress, he or she is also concerned to question the deeper assumptions someone makes about the world, because deeper assumptions give power to unhelpful intrusive thought patterns.

Ways in Which Problem Solving Helps

- Defines the problem
- Divides it into manageable parts
- Provides alternative solutions
- Selects the best solution
- Carries it out and examines results

The first task is to help you become aware of any unhelpful thinking and to recognise the relationship between it and emotional states. This can be done by helping you to recognise unhelpful thoughts during treatment when the stressful episode can be relived using role play.

The second task is to help you to develop different ways of interpreting events. You may be encouraged to stand back from a problem to get a more objective view. Different ideas may be sought, and you may be asked to rate their correctness. Once you are able to think of alternative ways of interpreting events, you may be asked to keep a daily record of stressful feelings and associated thoughts. You may be asked to reason with your intrusive unhelpful thoughts and suggest other possible interpretations to yourself as soon as a stressful feeling becomes apparent.

The th[illegible]d phase of the pr[illegible]ess is to encourage you to te[illegible] out the beliefs and atti[illegible]udes associated with stressful feelings in a systematic way. Instead of treating ideas as fact, you will be helped to see that it is possible to discover the degree of truth or otherwise of your beliefs through enquiry.

As you improve and learn the cognitive approach, the focus of treatment moves to deeper assumptions which are thought to underlie unhelpful thinking patterns. Unless these are identified and modified you are likely to become stressed again in the future. As these beliefs have usually been present from an early age, they tend to be resistant to change.

There are no simple ways of highlighting these faulty assumptions, but a useful start is for you to identify recurring stress themes in your life. The best way to break the pattern is to encourage you to act against these deep assumptions.

Approximately 15 sessions over three months are needed for most people requiring this specialist treatment. Two sessions a week are usually held in the first month followed by weekly meetings thereafter.

SOCIAL APPROACHES

These cover all efforts to improve a patient's well-being by changing aspects of his or her social life, particularly in regard to family relationships, work and leisure activities. Of course, defined in this way virtually all treatment consists of some social elements – even visiting the GP can be regarded as a social event.

At the most simple level, having a holiday, taking time off work and taking up a new interest are all important social means of trying to relieve stress. Education, sports, music, art, nature, science and religion all offer great opportunities for social encounters that can improve mental and physical well-being.

FAMILY THERAPY

More complicated forms of treatment also contain a strong social ingredient. Family approaches to treatment, sometimes called family therapy, treat the person in relation to their family. This does not mean that the family unit is held responsible for the individual's stress, but it is clear that many of the problems of stress revolve around difficulties in the way family members communicate and relate to each other. Bringing an entire family together for group discussions can sometimes be a very powerful way of helping everyone 'pull together instead of apart', of improving communication and of helping parents to develop a better relationship with their children and vice versa.

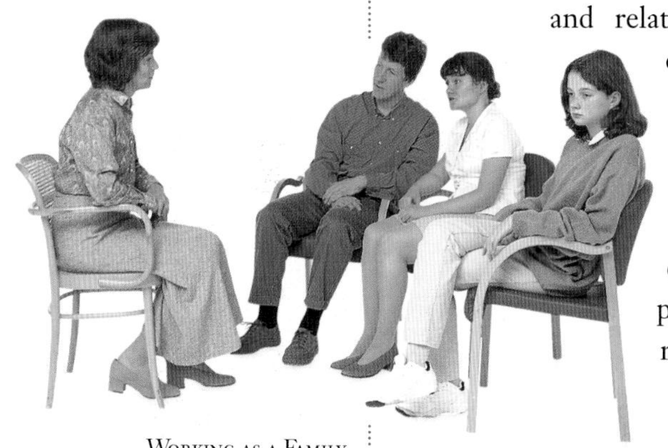

WORKING AS A FAMILY
It is sometimes useful for the whole family to attend therapy sessions. It may help to deal with a difficult relationship between parent and child.

GROUP THERAPY

Through discussing problems freely in a group over a period of a few weeks or months, this type of therapy helps combat social isolation, reminding people with high stress levels that they are not alone, and provides the opportunity for mutual encouragement and discussion of practical ways of overcoming stress.

Art therapy, play therapy, dance therapy, movement therapy, drama therapy, music therapy and gymnastics can all help people develop new social skills as well as practise old ones, increasing self-confidence and self-sufficiency. All aim to provide enjoyment, diversion, stimulation, increased self-esteem and a sense of individual achievement in a social context.

COMPARING TREATMENTS

The best treatment or therapy is the one that works for you. All methods have been found helpful by some people, and if one does not seem to be working after a fair trial you should try another treatment until you find some relief from your stress. The variety of psychological and social therapies can be confusing, so I have listed and defined the main ones (see pp.68–69).

MEDIA AND INTERNET

Newspapers, books, magazines, television, radio and the Internet aim to entertain, inform and instruct. Although they are usually passive forms of communication, when used selectively they may be useful in providing practical information about a wide range of interests and give temporary relief from stress by diverting your attention from personal worries.

USING THE TELEPHONE

The telephone gives you confidential access to an enormous number of counselling organisations across the world. The best-known source of confidential telephone contact is The Samaritans. This organisation has a 24-hour telephone service which is provided in the main by part-time volunteers of all ages and from all walks of life who have specialist training in counselling but whose main strength lies in their ability and willingness to listen to their callers sympathetically.

HELP ON THE LINE
Make use of the many telephone helplines staffed by volunteers who are trained to listen.

Types of Therapy Available

There are several different types of therapy available to stress sufferers. The following list of the most commonly used therapies also details some of the benefits of each.

SUPPORT & COUNSELLING

- Aims to help you help yourself by understanding why you feel the way you do and planning how to cope with emotional and practical realities.
- Helps you to live the life you have chosen by discussing current problems and alternative practical solutions.
- Provides a considerable amount of social support over several weeks or months.

BEHAVIOURAL THERAPY

- Believes that behaviour is 'learned' and can therefore be 'unlearned' or changed.
- Aims to stop you behaving in unhelpful or unwanted ways and to learn new patterns of behaviour that will make your life more enjoyable.
- Concentrates on how you behave at present and not on theories about why you learned to behave in certain ways. Usually lasts several months.

PSYCHOTHERAPY

- Talking is the main tool of treatment, and the different methods encourage talking about different aspects of your condition.
- Sessions usually take place weekly over a period of six to nine months.
- Supportive psychotherapy provides regular reassurance and encouragement. Sessions are informal and take place less frequently than formal psychotherapy – about once a month.

FAMILY THERAPY

- Views you as a member of a family or similar social group.
- Is concerned with how the members of the family or group communicate with each other and with their relationships.
- Aims to resolve distress and conflict without apportioning blame using psychotherapeutic methods over several months.

Types of Therapy Available (cont'd)

GROUP THERAPY

- This comprises a group of people, who did not know each other before, coming together with a therapist to help each other with their problems.
- Groups may be made up of people with the same problem or different problems, and they may be single sex or mixed.
- Group members can see that they are not alone in having problems and can get a great deal of support from other members of the group. Usually lasts some months.

COGNITIVE THERAPY (ALSO KNOWN AS COGNITIVE-BEHAVIOUR THERAPY)

- Based on the theory that changes in our emotions and behaviour are determined by our thoughts about events that occur. If we always take a gloomy or frightened view of life, we will interpret everything that happens in a negative way.
- Aims to help you recognise and change unhelpful and gloomy ways of thinking.
- Incorporates some parts of behaviour therapy.
- The average course is 12–20 sessions.

PSYCHOANALYSIS

- Believes that our behaviour and mental state originate in early experiences in childhood.
- Different methods of psychoanalysis interpret the meaning of what you say differently.
- A great deal of time is spent discussing the relationship between you and the therapist – this is taken to represent the relationship between you and important people in your early life such as your mother or father.
- Psychotherapy sessions take place several times a week over a period of years, so the treatment can be costly in terms of both time and money.

The Benefits of Self-Help Groups

There are many benefits to be gained from being a member of a self-help group. The following are just a few examples.

- These are groups of people who have a common problem and have joined together to do something about it.
- They are small, voluntary groups providing mutual aid, working together towards the accomplishment of a common aim, and providing members with support and help.
- People with stressful problems can feel lonely, confused and isolated, and it can help to talk about these problems with others 'in the same boat'.
- Support may be given individually or in a group. It may be aimed at helping the individual to adjust to a situation or to take steps to change it. It may be offered in crises or be available over a longer term.
- Self-help groups provide a wealth of information to help people cope more easily.
- Some forms of help needed to cope with particular problems can be provided directly by mutual aid organisations. These may be provided on a casual or informal basis, or they may be provided more formally. They may be carried out by group members on a voluntary basis, or they may involve hired staff. One example might be a choice between a friend baby-sitting or using an established playgroup. A few groups even provide services jointly with their local authority.
- Many self-help groups consider that the benefits and services provided by the state are inadequate, so they form pressure groups to bring about favourable changes.

RUNNING ITS COURSE

Perhaps the most neglected treatment of all is time. Mild stress can get better on its own, given time, and spontaneous improvement over six to 12 weeks is the norm. Quite a lot of people do get better anyway, sometimes in spite of treatment! Spontaneous natural improvement is most likely, however:

- In a first episode of stress;
- When the stress started recently;
- Where the stress started suddenly;
- When relatives and friends can give practical and emotional support.

KEY POINTS

- Family and friends can provide valuable support in dealing with stress.
- If you are worried about stress, the earlier you tackle it and help begins the better.
- There are three main types of professional help available: medical, psychological and social.
- Give a treatment a fair chance to help you before trying something else.
- Self-help groups and the media can provide a wealth of information, advice and practical help.

'False friends'

Smoking tobacco, drinking excess alcohol and taking drugs of dependence (sometimes even sleeping tablets, benzodiazepines or tranquillisers prescribed by the doctor, if not carefully monitored) make stress worse; they are habits that are unwise and should be stopped or severely curtailed.

They are false friends because they provide the illusion of temporary relief, making the processes of defence and successful adaptation much more difficult. People under stress sometimes attempt to cope, either deliberately or unconsciously, by using these substances to deal with the symptoms they are experiencing, or to withstand the pressure that they feel under.

MAKING MATTERS WORSE *Smoking and drinking heavily are major health hazards. Neither of these habits should be used as a means of combating stress.*

ALCOHOL

Alcohol in moderation may be a pleasure, but it is a potentially addictive drug with many subtle and complicated effects. Any long-standing stressful situation invites the serious risk of heavy drinking and eventual dependence on alcohol, which can wreck marriages, family and social life, careers and health (and, of course, you should never drive after drinking).

Recognising a Unit of Alcohol

Various drinks contain different amounts of alcohol. A unit of alcohol is equivalent to approximately 8–10 grams of pure alcohol.

Small glass of sherry = 1 unit

Small glass of wine = 1 unit

½ pint of beer or cider, or ¼ pint of strong lager = 1 unit

Single measure of aperitif or spirit = 1 unit

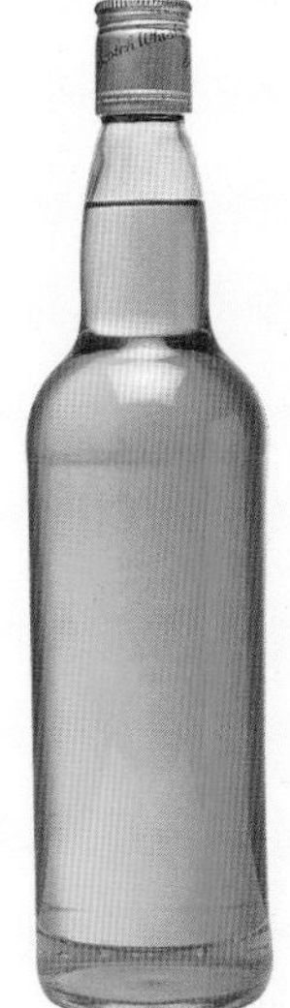

A standard bottle of spirits (brandy, gin, whisky) = 30 units

A 'unit' of alcohol may be defined as the equivalent of half an ordinary pint of beer or cider, a single measure of sherry or Martini, a single measure of spirits or a small glass of wine. The average man or woman will react to units of alcohol as shown in the table showing the effects of alcohol (see p.74), with women affected at lower 'doses' than men, the effects being increased by factors such as lack of food, tiredness and stress – and rapid consumption.

INCREASING DEPENDENCE ON ALCOHOL

The main signs that you may be developing a dependence on alcohol are:

- Awareness of a compulsion to drink;
- Developing a daily drinking pattern;
- Drinking takes priority over other activities;
- Your tolerance for alcohol changes – this usually increases at first but eventually falls;
- Repeated symptoms of alcohol withdrawal – nausea, headache, nervousness, shaking, sweating, tenseness, jitteriness, being 'on edge';
- Relief or avoidance of withdrawal symptoms by further consumption of alcohol;
- A very rapid return of the features of dependence after a period of abstinence.

Not all these signs may be present, and any one may occur to variable degrees in different people.

'SAFE DRINKING'

Safe levels of drinking are difficult to define precisely for each person, and depend on factors such as sex, body size and constitution. The levels are lower for women than for men.

What is a sensible limit? A unit of alcohol is as described earlier, and medical ad[illegible]s that the

The Effects of Alcohol

This chart shows the progressive effects, both mental and physical, of increasing quantities of alcohol consumption.

UNITS	EFFECTS
1–2	Feeling good and relaxed, but reaction time noticeably reduced.
2–4	Some loss of inhibition with poor judgement. Accidents become more likely.
3–5	Noticeable loss of inhibition, with physical clumsiness.
4–7+	Loss of physical control. Obviously drunk with extreme reactions. Above this level there is progressive loss of consciousness by degrees.

Tips to Help Cut Down Drinking

When attempting to cut down your alcohol consumption, you may find it helpful to follow the advice below, particularly during the first few weeks.

- Reduce the overall amount by stopping drinking at certain times, for example, lunch time, and do something else instead.
- Keep busy: plan activities that will keep your mind off drink.
- Avoid reminders of drinking and, whenever possible, places where alcohol will be consumed or people will offer you a drink.
- Plan avoidance action for times when you are confronted by these particular situations.
- Drink a long soft drink to quench your thirst before starting on alcohol.
- Allow yourself only one alcoholic drink an hour at any drinking session.
- Add mixers to wines and spirits to increase the volume and so help slow down consumption.
- Avoid drinking in 'rounds' if you are likely to break the above rules.

limit for men should be no more than 21 units a week and, for women, up to 14 units a week (if pregnant, alcohol probably should be avoided). The units should be spread over the week, with two or three drink-free days.

How much is too much? For men, 36 units or more in a week, and for women 22 units or more in a week. It is worth remembering that, on average, it takes one hour for the body to get rid of the alcohol in one unit. Remember that what others choose to drink is irrelevant to your health. Try to find some non-alcoholic alternative in drinking situations.

A man who drinks eight or more units a day (56 a week), or a woman who drinks more than five units a day (35 a week) is at great risk of developing an alcohol-rel[illegible] problem.

You may find it useful to involve a supportive relative or friend who can put up a united resistance with you.

SMOKING

The most common reason that cigarette smokers give for not stopping smoking is stress, but cutting out (or certainly cutting down) smoking should be the number one health priority. Tell a smoker that his habit is killing him, however, and the first thing he will probably decide to do is light a cigarette!

The most important step in giving up is the decision that you really do want to stop.

Once you make that decision you are halfway there. If you feel you need some help, it may be worth considering some form of nicotine replacement therapy (NRT): anything from nicotine gum to nicotine patches, the latter being worn on the skin for either 12- or 24-hour periods (depending on which kind you opt for). Both work by allowing the body to adjust gradually to lower amounts of nicotine. The gum is available on

DECEPTIVE BENEFITS
Many people rely on cigarettes to help them relax, but the smoking habit creates an extremely unhealthy dependence.

prescription, although the patches can be bought from the chemist – the pharmacist will be able to advise you on the type of NRT that is most appropriate for you.

However, it is well worth remembering that all these replacements are aids, not cures.

Unfortunately, the reasons for stopping smoking actually make it harder to stop. First, because they create a feeling of sacrifice (being forced to give up a little friend, prop, pleasure or however the smoker views cigarettes) and, second, because they create a bind – we do not smoke for the reasons we should stop – which prevents us from asking ourselves the real reasons for wanting or needing to smoke.

Remember that you had no need to smoke before you became hooked. The first cigarette probably tasted awful, and you had to work quite hard to become addicted. The most annoying part is that non-smokers do not seem to be missing out on anything; in fact, smokers keep smoking to achieve the same state of 'tranquillity' as non-smokers. So why do you smoke? Forget about stress, boredom and all the other reasons you may think you have; there are two real reasons – nicotine addiction and brainwashing.

Questions to Help You Give up Smoking

- What is smoking actually doing for me?
- Do I actually enjoy it?
- Do I really need to go through life spending a fortune just to stick these things in my mouth and make myself ill?

NICOTINE ADDICTION

Nicotine is one of the fastest-acting addictive drugs known to humankind. The concentration in the bloodstream falls quickly, however, to about half, in some 30 minutes after finishing a cigarette and then decreases to only a quarter within an hour. The withdrawal pangs from nicotine are so subtle that most smokers do not even realise that they are drug addicts.

Fortunately, nicotine is a relatively easy drug to 'kick' once you have accepted that this is the case. There is no physical pain, just an empty, restless feeling – the feeling of something missing.

If withdrawal is a prolonged process, the smoker may become irritable, nervous, insecure, agitated, lacking in confidence and irritable. These withdrawal symptoms make it very difficult for you to want to stop smoking. Within seconds of lighting a cigarette, nicotine is supplied to the bloodstream, resulting in the feeling of relaxation, well-being and confidence that the cigarette gives.

As soon as this cigarette is put out, the chain starts again. The difficulty is that it is when you are not smoking that you suffer the feelings, and you do not, therefore, blame the cigarette. When you light up you get relief and so are fooled into believing that the cigarette is the cure for all the bad feelings. So we smoke to feed the little monster, but we decide when to do it and we do it more in stressful situations: when we need to concentrate, when we are bored and when we wish to relax.

BRAINWASHING

Nicotine addiction is not the only problem and it is relatively easy to cope with (the smoker does not, for instance, wake up through the night craving a cigarette).

Another major difficulty is 'brainwashing'. The unconscious is a very powerful element in our minds, and despite a whole host of anti-smoking campaigns, we are still bombarded with extremely clever advertising which

Six Steps to Giving Up Smoking

Once you have made up your mind to stop smoking, you have to be very determined to succeed. Follow these steps and you will find that giving up is not as difficult as you feared.

STEP 1 You decide that you really want to do it, and realise that you can achieve your goal. Remember that smokers are not weak-willed and that it is only indecision that makes giving up more difficult.

STEP 2 Recognise and think about the fact that you are addicted to nicotine, but remember that withdrawal is not as painful as you think it is going to be, and that it takes only about three weeks to rid the body of 99% of the nicotine.

STEP 3 Look forward to the freedom. Do not be afraid of losing the prop you have been brainwashed into believing you need. Smoking enslaves you, preventing you from achieving the peace and confidence you used to have as a non-smoker.

STEP 4 Stop smoking completely. There is no such thing as just having one cigarette – smoking is a drug addiction and a chain reaction. By moping about one cigarette, you are punishing yourself needlessly.

STEP 5 Watch out for smokers – they may feel threatened by the fact that you have given up, and may try to tempt you back.

STEP 6 Remind yourself that there is nothing to give up and that there are enormous positive gains to be made by not smoking.

tells us that cigarettes relax us and give us confidence, and that the most precious thing on earth is a cigarette. Once addicted to nicotine, the power of the advertising is increased, which simply enforces the fear of giving up.

KEY POINTS

- Smoking, drinking alcohol and taking drugs of dependence are not a cure for stress – they all make stress, and coping with stress, harder.
- While alcohol in moderation can be a pleasure, heavy drinking carries serious risks to health and well-being – personal, family and at work.
- Stress is the most common reason smokers give for not stopping smoking.
- Nicotine is one of the fastest-acting addictive drugs known to humankind.
- Smoking is not only capable of ruining your health, it also ruins your finances.

Pills, potions and complementary methods

We are experiencing an increasing national dependence on drugs, pills and painkillers of all kinds. We are in danger of reaching the point where we believe that every ache, pain or worry must be soothed away by taking some kind of treatment, encouraging the idea that any form of stress is harmful.

There is a strong link between an overtly pill-conscious society and one that includes a growing number of people dependent on drugs. Some varieties of sleeping tablet and tranquilliser show this connection by the pleasurable effects they induce in vulnerable people. Experiencing these pleasurable effects may lead to dependence and can bring all the complications of dependence on stronger drugs, including withdrawal symptoms if they are stopped and a desperate need to have a good supply in case they are needed.

COMPLEMENTARY THERAPIES *Many people are turning to complementary therapies such as yoga and meditation to help them cope with the stress in their lives.*

Many people find complementary therapies of benefit. They are becoming increasingly popular and include, among many others, yoga, meditation, autogenic training, biofeedback, acupuncture, Alexander technique and aromatherapy. Some of these are available at little or no cost, others may prove to be more expensive.

AVOIDING DEFENCE MECHANISMS

Adapting to stress is a two-stage process. First, we have to realise that some of our repeated responses to continuing stress may be unhelpful; second, we need to explore and use new ways of coping until satisfactory solutions are found.

You may sometimes hear social workers, counsellors and psychologists using words such as 'denial' and 'rationalisation' to describe the way people respond to stress. These are technical terms which most people do not come across in everyday speech. I explain them briefly over the next page or so.

Some of these repeated, unhelpful responses – defence mechanisms – are described below. Remember, though, that these are only ideas that may help us understand ourselves by showing how our minds work and how we react to stress.

- Compensation – a behaviour that is developed to offset a defect or sense of inferiority, for example, running a pet sanctuary to make up for poor human relationships. Thus overcompensation occurs when compensation is overdone.
- Conversion – hidden fears may be 'converted' and come to the surface in the form of bodily symptoms. Someone who is afraid of going out may develop a weakness in the

- Denial – persuading oneself that there is nothing really wrong when, in fact, there is. This is done in the hope that the trouble will somehow go away – for example, refusing to admit that you are ill.
- Displacement – shifting an emotion from one target to another. Ideas or attitudes which make us uncomfortable may be disguised or avoided in this way. For example, anger with our workmates may be taken out on our families.
- Dissociation – avoiding looking too closely at our attitudes so that inconsistencies in our thoughts and conduct are overlooked.
- Fixation – 'fixed' personal behaviour which is more appropriate to earlier, less mature periods. This is seen in grown adults who depend, child-like, on others.
- Identification – conscious or unconscious modelling of oneself on another person, which may include the assumption of his or her dress, leisure activities, etc. This may be quite normal: for example, young people often imitate the attitudes and behaviour of older people whom they hold in high regard.
- Introjection – the turning inwards on oneself of the feelings and attitudes towards others, which gives rise to conflict and aggression. Unspoken anger with other family members may then lead to self-harm.
- Inversion – the exaggeration of tendencies opposite to those that are repressed. Prudery, for example, may be an inversion of repressed sexual desire.
- Projection – the opposite of introjection, the displacement of personal attitudes on to others or the environment. This is another way of avoiding self-blame and guilt. Personal inadequacies are blamed on others or even on the environment.

- Rationalisation – a form of self-deception in which socially acceptable reasons are found for conduct that is prompted by less worthy motives.
- Regression – going back to the ways of thinking, feeling and behaving which are more appropriate to earlier stages of individual or social development. Thus, an adult may regress to childish temper tantrums.
- Repression – the pushing out of consciousness of ideas and impulses that do not fit in with what the individual regards as correct in the circumstances. Repression is unconscious and involuntary, in contrast to suppression, which is the intentional refusal to have thoughts or feelings, or carry out actions that conflict with moral standards.
- Resistance – a barrier between the unconscious and conscious mind, preventing the resolution of tensions or conflicts. For example, someone might unconsciously resist enquiring into the origins of his stress, thereby prolonging his condition.
- Sublimation – the direction of undesirable or forbidden tendencies into more socially acceptable channels. For example, childish, self-indulgent behaviour is sublimated into entertaining or altruistic social behaviour in the process of maturity. Surplus energy may be sublimated into useful channels.
- Transference – the experience of emotions towards one person which are derived from experience with another. For example, anxious or hostile feelings previously felt towards a domineering parent may, in later life, be felt in relation to figures of authority.
- Withdrawal – giving up, and physical and emotional retirement from a stressful situation, characterised by loss of enthusiasm and [illegible]erest, apathy and daydreaming.

Golden Rules for Reducing Stress

Stress is unhealthy only if you have too much of it. Keep your stress at a manageable level by following these essential tips.

- Get your priorities right – sort out what really matters in your life.
- Think ahead, and try to anticipate how to get round difficulties.
- Share your worries with family or friends whenever possible.
- Try to develop a social network or circle of friends.
- Exercise regularly.
- Lead a regular lifestyle.
- Give yourself treats and rewards for positive actions, attitudes and thoughts.
- Get to know yourself better – improve your defences and strengthen your weak points.
- Think realistically about problems, and decide to take some appropriate action; if necessary, distract yourself in a pleasant way – don't 'bottle things up' or sit up all night brooding.
- Try to keep things in proportion.
- Don't be too hard on yourself.
- Seek medical help if you are worried about your health.
- There are always people who are willing and able to help, whatever the problem – don't be unwilling to benefit from their experience.
- Relax and take short rests throughout the day.
- Make small, regular changes to your lifestyle.
- Learn to delegate.
- Make space for leisure time.
- Have proper breaks for meals.
- Make time for yourself every day and every week.
- Listen carefully to those around you.
- Enjoy yourself, and your family and friends.

Complementary Methods

Many complementary methods and treatments are available that can be used to alleviate stress. This chart gives details of some of the most easily accessible and successful methods.

YOGA

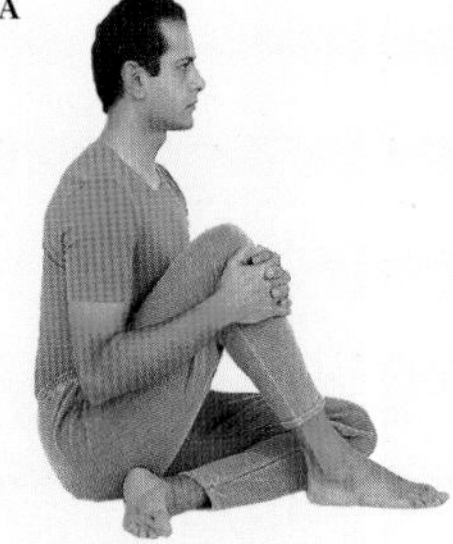

This is a useful technique for physical and mental relaxation and consists of exercises in physical posture to condition the body. Mastery is reckoned by the ability to hold the postures for an extended period without involuntary movement or physical distractions. Instruction emphasising both the physical and spiritual benefits of yoga techniques is widely available.

MEDITATION

This consists of a number of techniques of concentration and contemplation, which can be effective in controlling pulse and respiratory rates, and in the control of migraine and high blood pressure. Transcendental meditation has been reported to help through reduction of tension, lowering anxiety, increasing job satisfaction and improving work performance. Meditators spend two daily 20-minute sessions in a quiet, comfortable place, silently repeating their mantra.

AUTOGENIC TRAINING

This method of self-hypnosis emphasises individual control over bodily processes through specific exercises. Training usually takes between two and three months, and you learn standard training exercises aimed at inducing a feeling of well-being and coping ability. Specific exercises deal with, for example, breathing, blood flow and skin temperature. Profound muscular relaxation is achievable.

Complementary Methods (cont'd)

BIOFEEDBACK

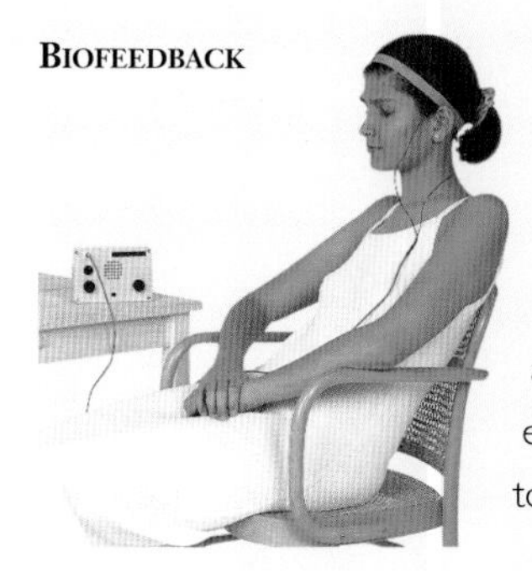

Information supplied instantaneously about your bodily processes, for example, blood pressure or heart rate, is monitored electronically and 'fed back' to you by a gauge on a meter, a light or a sound. You learn to detect physical reactions and establish control over them. It can help alleviate symptoms such as pain and muscle tension, and its effects can be lasting if used in combination with counselling to help the person understand reactions to stress.

ACUPUNCTURE

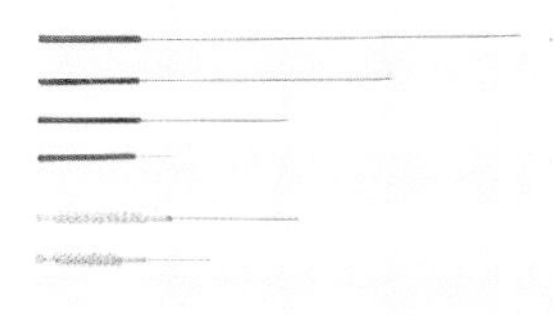

This is a traditional, ancient Chinese medical technique for relieving pain, curing disease and improving general health. It consists of inserting needles into any of hundreds of points located over various 'meridians'. It is a treatment that aims to alter the flow of an individual's bodily energy or life force to relieve pain and restore physical and mental health.

ALEXANDER TECHNIQUE

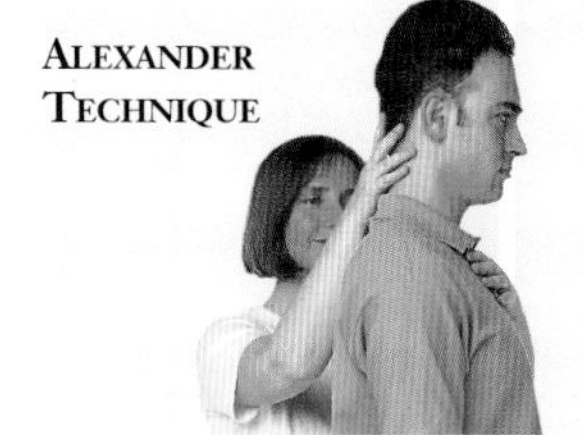

This technique teaches people new ways of thinking and using their bodies with a view to eliminating the effects of unconscious bad habits, such as tension and contorted posture, thereby improving physical and psychological well-being. It is a way of life rather than a therapy.

AROMATHERAPY

Pure essential oils (obtained from aromatic plants by steam distillation) are used to soothe tension and improve health and mental well-being. The oils are usually massaged into the body, but may be inhaled, blended or used in baths. Essential oils can temporarily alter our moods and release stress.

USING THE GOLDEN RULES

If you stick to the Golden Rules (see p.85), you will help yourself become calmer and more relaxed. You will have to keep working at it to get the full benefit: work out a practical routine and stick to it, not just for a few days. And remember to enjoy yourself – that is the best cure for stress. Learn to relax and take things easy for at least an hour each day – a warm bath, taking your time, enjoying pleasant feelings, a relaxing walk or reading an interesting book can help release you from the things that cause you stress.

Breathe deeply and gently, count to 10, and think again. Take one day at a time – learn to accept a bad day, as tomorrow may be better.

CONCLUSION

Although we cannot, and indeed must not, avoid stress, we can learn to meet it efficiently and live with it successfully, rather than letting stress overwhelm us to the extent that it affects both our mental and physical health.

RELAXING IN THE BATH
Make time every day to do something enjoyable. Proper relaxation is the best way to reduce stress.

Because of the enormous individual differences in the causes of stress, and in our abilities to cope, this book cannot hope to give all the answers to everyone's problems. What I have tried to do, however, is to help you think about, and identify, the undesirable stresses in your own life, and learn how to control these – either alone or with the help of others.

Taking stock of ourselves and our lives from time to time can only be an extremely beneficial exercise. It is amazing how little we normally question our priorities and how many sources of unnecessary stress we can get rid of by doing just that.

Key Points

- Becoming dependent on pills and potions creates further problems.
- Many people find complementary methods such as yoga of benefit.
- Overcome stress by understanding and controlling your response to it.
- Remember to use the golden rules for reducing stress.

Useful addresses

Accept Services
(alcohol-related problems)
724 Fulham Road,
London SW6 5SE
Tel: (0171) 371 7477

Age Concern England
Astral House,
1268 London Road,
London SW16 4ER
Tel: (0181) 679 8000

Alcoholics Anonymous
London Region Telephone Service
(10 a.m.–10 p.m., 7 days a week;
answerphone at other times)
Tel: (0171) 352 3001

Alzheimer's Disease Society
Gordon House,
10 Greencoat Place,
London SW1P 1PH
Tel: (0171) 306 0606

Association for Post-Natal Illness
25 Jerdan Place,
Fulham, London SW6 1BE
Tel: (0171) 386 0868

British Association for Counselling (BAC)
1 Regent Place, Rugby CV21 2PJ
Tel: (01788) 578328

The Brook Advisory Service
Service for under-25s offering advice
on all aspects of sexual health
Helpline (Mon–Thurs 9 a.m.–5 p.m.,
Fri 9 a.m.–4 p.m.)
Tel: (0171) 713 9000
24-hour message line
Tel: (0171) 617 8000

Carers National Association
20–25 Glasshouse Yard,
London EC1A 4JT
Tel: (0345) 573369 (local rate)
Mon–Fri 10 a.m.–12 noon,
2 p.m.–4 p.m.

Childline
(for children requiring counselling)
Freephone: (0800) 1111

Compassionate Friends
53 North Street,
Bristol BS3 1EN
Tel: (01179) 539639

Cruse Bereavement Care
Cruse House,
126 Sheen Road,
Richmond, Surrey TW9 1UR
Tel: (0181) 940 4818
(Mon–Fri 9.30 a.m.–4 p.m.).
Helpline (recorded message)
Tel: (0181) 332 7227

Fellowship of Depressives Anonymous
(Self-help group for people who suffer from depression and their carers – local groups in England)
36 Chestnut Avenue, Beverley,
East Yorkshire HU17 9QU
Tel: (01482) 860619

Eating Disorders Association
1st Floor, Wensum House,
103 Prince of Wales Road,
Norwich NR1 1DW
National helpline
(Mon–Fri 9 a.m.–6.30 p.m.)
Tel: (01603) 621414
Youth helpline (4 p.m.–6 p.m., answerphone at other times)
Tel: (01603) 765050

Family Planning Association
Tel: (0171) 837 5432
Contraceptive helpline: (0171) 837 4044

Gamblers Anonymous
Tel: (0171) 384 3040

Help the Aged
16–18 St James's Walk,
London EC1R 0BE
Tel: (0171) 253 0253

Local Health Information Office
Freephone: (0800) 665544
All health authorities now have a health information service, obtainable by dialling the number above. This same number applies to the whole country, and puts you through to service local to you. This service should be able to tell you the contact numbers for local voluntary groups, and some services have recorded facts about common disorders.

Manic Depression Fellowship
8–10 High Street,
Kingston-upon-Thames, Surrey KT1 1EY
Tel: (0181) 974 6550

MIND
(The National Association for Mental Health)
Tel: (0181) 519 2122

National AIDS Helpline
Tel: (0800) 567123

National Association for Bereavement Services
20 Norton Folgate,
Liverpool Street, London E1 6DB
Helpline: (0171) 247 1080

National Association of Victims Support Schemes
Cranmer House,
39 Brixton Road, London SW9 6DZ
Tel: (0171) 735 9166

National Family Mediation
9 Tavistock Place,
London WC1H 9SN
Tel: (0171) 383 5993

The National Phobic Society
407 Wilbraham Road,
Chorlton,
Manchester M21 0UT
Tel: (0161) 881 1937

Nexus
(an association of unattached people looking to widen their social circles; not a helpline)
Mon–Fri 11 a.m.–7 p.m.
Tel: (0181) 367 6328

Parentline
Endway House,
The Endway,
Hadleigh,
Essex SS7 2AN
Helpline: (01702) 559900
Support for troubled parents in times of stress or crisis, chiefly through a confidential and anonymous telephone helpline.

Parent Network
Room 2,
Winchester House,
11 Cranmer Road,
London SW9 6EJ
Tel: (0171) 735 1214

Relate National Marriage Guidance
Herbert Gray College,
Little Church Street,
Rugby CV21 3AP
Tel: (01788) 573241

Release
(drug-related problems)
388 Old Street,
London EC1V 9LT
Tel: (0171) 729 9904

Samaritans
46 Marshall Street,
London W1V 1LR
Tel: (0171) 734 2800
24-hour national helpline: (0345) 909090
See local phone book for nearest local helpline number.

Stillbirth and Neonatal Death Society (SANDS)
28 Portland Place,
London W1N 4DE
Helpline: (0171) 436 5881
(Mon–Fri 10 a.m.–5 p.m.)
Administration & publications
Tel: (0171) 436 7940

Terence Higgins Trust
Tel: (0171) 242 1010
(12 noon–10 p.m. daily)
24-hour national helpline: (0800) 567123

The Thanet Phobic Group
47 Orchard Road,
Westbrook,
Margate, Kent CT9 5JS
Tel: (01843) 833720

Westminster Pastoral Foundation
(counselling)
Tel: (0171) 937 6956

Index

Acknowledgements

PUBLISHER'S ACKNOWLEDGEMENTS

Dorling Kindersley would like to thank the following for their help and participation in this project:

Editorial: Nicola Munro; **Design:** Adam Powers; **DTP:** Rachel Symons; **Consultancy:** Dr. Sue Davidson; **Indexing:** Indexing Specialists; **Administration:** Christopher Gordon.

Organisations: St. John's Ambulance, St. Andrew's Ambulance Organisation, British Red Cross.

Photography: (p.30, p.73) Paul Mattock; **Picture research:** Angela Anderson; **Picture librarian:** Charlotte Oster.

PICTURE CREDITS

The publisher would like to thank the following for their kind permission to reproduce their photographs. Every effort has been made to trace the copyright holders. Dorling Kindersley apologises for any unintentional omissions and would be pleased, in any such cases, to add an acknowledgement in future editions.

Pictor Uniphoto p.37